D0331131

SECOND BAPTIST CHURCH
2000 FIRST STREET
GARLAND, TEXAS

JUNIOR HYMNAL

Compiled and Edited by
BILL F. LEACH
and
PAUL BOBBITT

Illustrated by James Padgett

BROADMAN PRESS
Nashville, Tennessee

© Copyright 1964 · BROADMAN PRESS

Nashville, Tennessee

All Rights Reserved
International Copyright Secured

451–230

Printed in the United States of America
100.JY64KSP

About Your Hymnal

This is your hymnal. It contains many wonderful hymns for you to sing and play. They have come from many countries of the world. Some of them are hundreds of years old. Many are friends which you already know. Some of them, however, are new and have been written especially for this hymnal. All of them have been carefully selected just for *you*.

We are grateful to the many persons who helped determine the contents of *Junior Hymnal*—ministers of music, choir directors, Sunday school teachers, and others who work with Juniors. It is impossible to list all of them. We do, however, wish to express special appreciation to those who shared most in the selections of the hymns. They are James C. Barry, Betty Brewer, Sibley Burnett, Richie Harris, Reuben Herring, Edward Hurt, Jr., William N. McElrath, Lillian Moore Rice, Margaret Sharp, Neta Stewart, and Frances Whitworth.

Junior Hymnal has been designed for you to use in all your church activities. You will also enjoy using it at home. Examine it from the front cover to the back cover. Become familiar with it. Study the indexes in the back. Learn how to quickly find hymns of praise, prayer, Thanksgiving, Christmas, Easter, and others. Memorize those you like best. Learn to use your hymnal as well as you use your Bible.

In the hope that you will learn to sing and love every hymn in this hymnal, we dedicate it to you.

Bill F. Leach
Paul Bobbitt

Make a joyful noise unto

the Lord, all ye lands.

Serve the Lord with gladness:

come before his presence with

singing.

Psalm 100:1, 2

9loves
2 stanzas

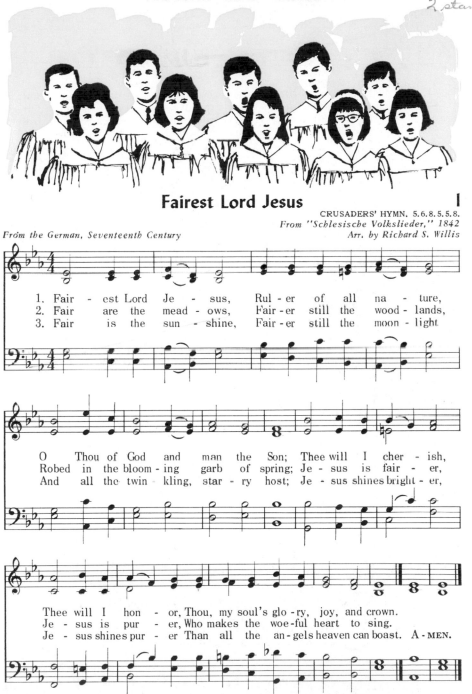

Fairest Lord Jesus

1

CRUSADERS' HYMN. 5.6.8.5.5.8.
From "Schlesische Volkslieder," 1842
Arr. by Richard S. Willis

From the German, Seventeenth Century

1. Fair - est Lord Je - sus, Rul - er of all na - ture,
2. Fair are the mead - ows, Fair - er still the wood - lands,
3. Fair is the sun - shine, Fair - er still the moon - light.

O Thou of God and man the Son; Thee will I cher - ish,
Robed in the bloom - ing garb of spring; Je - sus is fair - er,
And all the twin - kling, star - ry host; Je - sus shines bright - er,

Thee will I hon - or, Thou, my soul's glo - ry, joy, and crown.
Je - sus is pur - er, Who makes the woe - ful heart to sing.
Je - sus shines pur - er Than all the an - gels heaven can boast. A - MEN.

All Hail the Power of Jesus' Name

Edward Perronet
Alt. by John Rippon

CORONATION. C.M.
Oliver Holden

1. All hail the pow'r of Je - sus' name! Let an - gels pros - trate fall;
2. Ye cho - sen seed of Is - rael's race, Ye ran-somed from the fall,
3. Let ev - 'ry kin - dred, ev - 'ry tribe, On this ter - res - trial ball,
4. O that with yon - der sa - cred throng We at His feet may fall!

Bring forth the roy - al di - a - dem,
Hail Him who saves you by His grace,
To Him all maj - es - ty as - cribe,
We'll join the ev - er - last - ing song,

And crown Him Lord of all; Bring forth the roy - al
And crown Him Lord of all; Hail Him who saves you
And crown Him Lord of all; To Him all maj - es -
And crown Him Lord of all; We'll join the ev - er -

di - a - dem, And crown Him Lord of all.
by His grace, And crown Him Lord of all.
ty as - cribe, And crown Him Lord of all.
last - ing song, And crown Him Lord of all. A-MEN.

Praise to the Lord, the Almighty

3

Joachim Neander
Tr. by Catherine Winkworth

LOBE DEN HERREN. 14. 14. 4. 7. 8.
From "Praxis Pietatis Melica," 1668

1. Praise to the Lord, the Al-might-y, the King of cre-a - tion!
2. Praise to the Lord, who o'er all things so won-drous-ly reign - eth;
3. Praise to the Lord, who doth pros-per thy work and de-fend thee;
4. Praise to the Lord, O let all that is in me a-dore Him!

O my soul, praise Him, for He is thy health and sal-va - tion!
Shel-ters thee un-der His wings, yea, so gen-tly sus-tain - eth!
Sure-ly His good-ness and mer-cy here dai-ly at-tend thee.
All that hath life and breath, come now with prais-es be-fore Him.

All ye who hear, Now to His tem-ple draw near;
Hast thou not seen How thy de-sires e'er have been
Pon-der a-new What the Al-might-y can do,
Let the A-men Sound from His peo-ple a - gain,

Join me in glad ad-o-ra - tion!
Grant-ed in what He or-dain - eth?
If with His love He be-friend thee.
Glad-ly for aye we a-dore Him. A - MEN.

4   Come, Christians, Join to Sing

MADRID. 6.6.6.6.D.
Source Unknown
Har. by David Evans

Christian Henry Bateman

1. Come, Chris-tians, join to sing   Al - le - lu - ia! A - men!
2. Come, lift your hearts on high;   Al - le - lu - ia! A - men!
3. Praise yet our Christ a - gain;   Al - le - lu - ia! A - men!

Loud praise to Christ our King;   Al - le - lu - ia! A - men!
Let prais - es fill the sky;   Al - le - lu - ia! A - men!
Life shall not end the strain;   Al - le - lu - ia! A - men!

Let all, with heart and voice,   Be - fore His throne re - joice;
He is our Guide and Friend;   To us He'll con - de - scend;
On heav-en's bliss-ful shore   His good - ness we'll a - dore,

Praise is His gra - cious choice: Al - le - lu - ia! A - men!
His love shall nev - er end: Al - le - lu - ia! A - men!
Sing - ing for - ev - er - more,   "Al - le - lu - ia! A - men!"

With Happy Voices Ringing

BERTHOLD. 7.6.7.6.D.
Berthold Tours

William G. Tarrant

1. With hap-py voic-es ring-ing, Thy chil-dren, Lord, ap-pear;
2. For though no eye be-holds Thee, No hand Thy touch may feel,
3. And shall we not a-dore Thee, With more than joy-ous song,

Their joy-ous prais-es bring-ing In an-thems full and clear;
Thy u-ni-verse un-folds Thee, Thy star-ry heav'ns re-veal;
And live in truth be-fore Thee, All beau-ti-ful and strong?

For skies of gold-en splen-dor, For az-ure roll-ing sea,
The earth and all its glo-ry, Our homes and all we love
Lord, bless our souls' en-deav-or Thy serv-ants true to be,

For blos-soms sweet and ten-der, O Lord, we wor-ship Thee.
Tell forth the won-drous sto-ry Of One who reigns a-bove.
And through all life, for-ev-er, To live our praise to Thee.

6

Holy, Holy, Holy

Reginald Heber

NICAEA. 11. 12. 12. 10.
John B. Dykes

1. Ho-ly, ho-ly, ho-ly! Lord God Al-might-y! Ear-ly in the
2. Ho-ly, ho-ly, ho-ly! all the saints a-dore Thee, Cast-ing down their
3. Ho-ly, ho-ly, ho-ly! tho' the dark-ness hide Thee, Tho' the eye of
4. Ho-ly, ho-ly, ho-ly! Lord God Al-might-y! All Thy works shall

morn - ing our song shall rise to Thee; Ho-ly, ho-ly, ho - ly,
gold - en crowns a-round the glass-y sea; Cher-u-bim and ser-a-phim
sin - ful man Thy glo-ry may not see; On-ly Thou art ho - ly;
praise Thy name, in earth, and sky, and sea; Ho-ly, ho-ly, ho - ly;

mer - ci-ful and might-y! God in three Per-sons, bless-ed Trin-i-ty!
fall - ing down be-fore Thee, Who wert, and art, and ev-er-more shalt be.
there is none be-side Thee, Per-fect in pow'r, in love, and pur-i-ty.
mer - ci-ful and might-y! God in three Per-sons, bless-ed Trin-i-ty!

7

This Is the Day the Lord Hath Made

Isaac Watts

ARLINGTON. C.M.
Thomas A. Arne

1. This is the day the Lord hath made; He calls the hours His own;
2. To - day He rose and left the dead, And Sa-tan's em-pire fell;
3. Ho - san-na to th'a-noint-ed King, To Da-vid's ho-ly Son:
4. Blest be the Lord, who comes to men With mes-sag-es of grace;

Let heav'n re-joice, let earth be glad, And praise sur-round the throne.
To - day the saints His tri-umph spread, And all His won-ders tell.
Help us, O Lord! de-scend and bring Sal - va-tion from Thy throne.
Who comes, in God His Fa-ther's name, To save our sin-ful race.

O Worship the King

8

LYONS. 10. 10. 11. 11.

Robert Grant

Johann M. Haydn

1. O wor - ship the King, all glo-rious a - bove, And grate-ful - ly sing His
2. O tell of His might, O sing of His grace, Whose robe is the light, whose
3. Thy boun - ti - ful care what tongue can re - cite? It breathes in the air, it
4. Frail chil dren of dust, and fee - ble as frail, In Thee do we trust, nor

won - der - ful love; Our Shield and De - fend - er, the An - cient of Days,
can - o - py space! His char - iots of wrath the deep thun - der-clouds form,
shines in the light, It streams from the hills, it de - scends to the plain,
find Thee to fail: Thy mer - cies how ten - der, how firm to the end,

Pa - vil - ioned in splen-dor, and gird - ed with praise.
And dark is His path on the wings of the storm.
And sweet - ly dis - tils in the dew and the rain.
Our Mak - er, De - fend - er, Re - deem - er, and Friend. A - MEN.

9 We Praise Thee with Our Minds, O Lord

CLONMEL. C.M.D.
Irish Melody
Arr. by William J. Reynolds

Hugh T. McElrath

1. We praise Thee with our minds, O Lord, Kept sharp to think Thy thought;
2. We praise Thee through our bod-ies, Lord, Kept strong to do Thy will;
3. We praise Thee in our hearts, O King, Kept pure to know Thy ways;

Come, Ho-ly Ghost, with grace out-poured, To teach what Christ hath taught.
Thy Spir-it's tem-ples, which af-ford A means to praise Thee still.
And raise to Thee a hymn to sing E-ter-nal-ly Thy praise.

In all our learn-ing, may we seek That wis-dom from a-bove
We give our-selves a sac-ri-fice To live as un-to Thee;
Al-though a-dor-ing hearts will bow As age on a-ges roll;

Which comes to all: the brave, the meek, Who ask in faith and love.
For Thou a-lone hast paid the price To bring sal-va-tion free.
We praise Thee in our be-ings now, Mind, bod-y, heart, and soul. A-MEN.

Arrangement Copyright 1952, Broadman Press. Words ©Copyright 1964, Broadman Press. All rights
reserved. International copyright secured.

Praise the Lord! Ye Heavens, Adore Him

From the "Foundling Hospital Collection," 1796

HYFRYDOL, 8.7.8.7.D.
Rowland H. Prichard

1. Praise the Lord! ye heav'ns, a-dore Him; Praise Him, an-gels, in the height;
2. Praise the Lord! for He is glo-rious; Nev-er shall His prom-ise fail;

Sun and moon, re-joice be-fore Him; Praise Him, all ye stars of light.
God hath made His saints vic-to-rious, Sin and death shall not pre-vail.

Praise the Lord! for He hath spo-ken; Worlds His might-y voice o-beyed;
Praise the God of our sal-va-tion! Hosts on high, His pow'r pro-claim;

Law which nev-er shall be bro-ken For their guidance hath He made.
Heav'n and earth and all cre-a-tion Laud and mag-ni-fy His name.

11. We Praise Thee, O God, Our Redeemer

KREMSER. *Irregular*
Netherlands Folk Song
Arr. by Edward Kremser

Julia Cady Cory

1. We praise Thee, O God, our Re-deem-er, Cre-a-tor,
2. We wor-ship Thee, God of our fa-thers, we bless Thee;
3. With voic-es u-nit-ed our prais-es we of-fer,

In grate-ful de-vo-tion our trib-ute we bring.
Thro' life's storm and tem-pest our Guide hast Thou been.
To Thee, great Je-ho-vah, glad an-thems we raise.

We lay it be-fore Thee, we kneel and a-dore Thee,
When per-ils o'er-take us, es-cape Thou wilt make us,
Thy strong arm will guide us, our God is be-side us,

We bless Thy ho-ly name, glad prais-es we sing.
And with Thy help, O Lord, our bat-tles we win.
To Thee, our great Re-deem-er, for-ev-er be praise. A-MEN.

Words used by permission David C. Cory.

Let All the World in Every Corner Sing

ALL THE WORLD. *Irregular*
Robert G. McCutchan

George Herbert

12

1. Let all the world in ev - ery cor - ner sing: My God and
2. Let all the world in ev - ery cor - ner sing: My God and

King! The heav'ns are not too high, His praise may thith - er fly; The
King! The Church with psalms must shout, No door can keep them out: But,

earth is not too low, His prais - es there may grow. Let all the world in
more than all, the heart Must bear the long - est part. Let all the world in

ev - 'ry cor - ner sing: My God and King! God and King!

Music Copyright 1962, Renewal. Abingdon Press. Used by permission.

13   Lord Jesus, from Thy Throne Above

John R. Darbyshire

WORSHIP. C.M.
Traditional German Melody

1. Lord Je - sus, from Thy throne a - bove Be - hold us
2. Be - fore Thy throne in heav - en's height A - dor - ing
3. So now we lift our hearts to Thee, And in our

pray - ing here, And help us now by faith and love To
an - gels sing; But we be - lieve Thou dost de - light In
wor - ship raise, With all the com - pa - ny of heav'n, An

know Thy pres - ence near, To know Thy pres - ence near.
gifts Thy chil - dren bring, In gifts Thy chil - dren bring.
of - fer - ing of praise, An of - fer - ing of praise.

Copyright E. C. Schirmer Music Co. Used by permission.

14   Jesus, the Very Thought of Thee

Bernard of Clairvaux
Tr. by Edward Caswall

ST. AGNES. C.M.
John B. Dykes

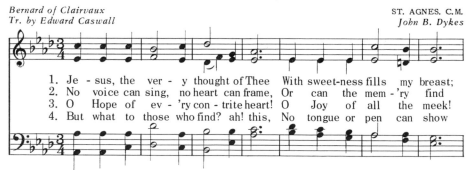

1. Je - sus, the ver - y thought of Thee With sweet-ness fills my breast;
2. No voice can sing, no heart can frame, Or can the mem - 'ry find
3. O Hope of ev - 'ry con - trite heart! O Joy of all the meek!
4. But what to those who find? ah! this, No tongue or pen can show

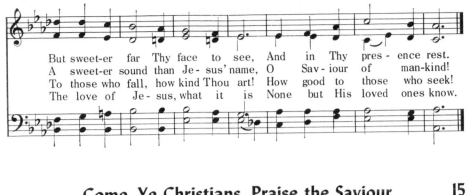

But sweet-er far Thy face to see, And in Thy pres - ence rest.
A sweet-er sound than Je - sus' name, O Sav - iour of man-kind!
To those who fall, how kind Thou art! How good to those who seek!
The love of Je - sus, what it is None but His loved ones know.

Come, Ye Christians, Praise the Saviour 15

JESUS, JESUS, NICHTS ALS JESUS. 8.7.8.7.7.7.
"Vollkommenes Choralbuch," 1715

Anonymous, alt.

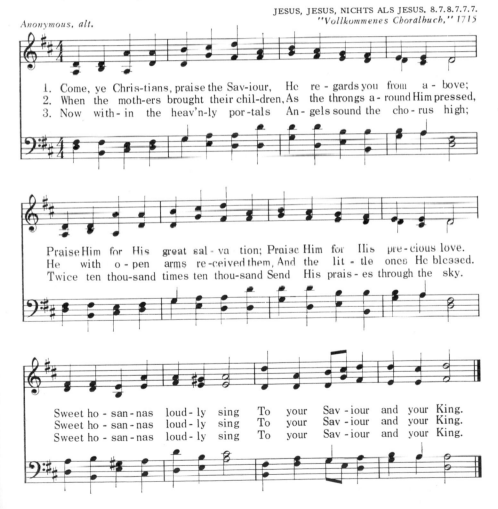

1. Come, ye Chris-tians, praise the Sav-iour, He re - gards you from a - bove;
2. When the moth-ers brought their chil-dren, As the throngs a - round Him pressed,
3. Now with-in the heav'n-ly por-tals An - gels sound the cho-rus high;

Praise Him for His great sal - va tion; Praise Him for His pre - cious love.
He with o - pen arms re -ceived them, And the lit - tle ones He blessed.
Twice ten thou-sand times ten thou-sand Send His prais - es through the sky.

Sweet ho - san-nas loud-ly sing To your Sav-iour and your King.
Sweet ho - san-nas loud-ly sing To your Sav-iour and your King.
Sweet ho - san-nas loud-ly sing To your Sav-iour and your King.

Singing for Jesus

SLANE. 10. 10. 10. 10.
Ancient Irish Traditional Melody
Harm. by David Evans

Frances R. Havergal

1. Sing - ing for Je - sus, our Sav - iour and King,
2. Sing - ing for Je - sus, our shep - herd and guide,
3. Sing - ing for Je - sus, yes, sing - ing for joy,

Sing - ing for Je - sus, the Lord whom we love;
Sing - ing for glad - ness of heart that He gives;
Thus will we praise Him and tell out His love;

All ad - o - ra - tion we joy - ous - ly bring,
Sing - ing for won - der and praise that He died,
Till He shall call us to bright - er em - ploy,

Long - ing to praise as they praise Him a - bove.
Sing - ing for bless - ing and joy that He lives.
Sing - ing for Je - sus, for - ev - er a - bove.

All Glory, Laud, and Honor

Theodulph of Orleans
Tr. by John M. Neale

ST. THEODULPH. 7.6.7.6.D.
Melchior Teschner

1. All glo - ry, laud, and hon - or, To Thee, Re - deem - er, King,
2. The com - pa - ny of an - gels Are prais - ing Thee on high,
3. To Thee, be - fore Thy pas - sion They sang their hymns of praise;

To whom the lips of chil - dren Made sweet ho - san - nas ring:
And mor - tal men and all things Cre - at - ed make re - ply:
To Thee, now high ex - alt - ed, Our mel - o - dy we raise:

Thou art the King of Is - ra - el, Thou Da - vid's roy - al Son,
The peo - ple of the He - brews With palms be - fore Thee went;
Thou didst ac - cept their prais - es; Ac - cept the praise we bring,

Who in the Lord's name com - est, The King and bless - ed One.
Our praise and prayer and an - thems Be - fore Thee we pre - sent.
Who in all good de - light - est, Thou good and gra - cious King.

I Love Thee

Anonymous

I LOVE THEE. 11. 11. 11. 11.
Ingall's "Christian Harmony," 1805

1. I love Thee, I love Thee, I love Thee, my Lord;
2. I'm hap - py, I'm hap - py, oh, won - drous ac - count!
3. O Je - sus, my Sav - iour, with Thee I am blest,
4. Oh, who's like my Sav - iour? He's Sa - lem's bright King;

I love Thee, my Sav - iour, I love Thee, my God:
My joys are im - mor - tal, I stand on the mount:
My life and sal - va - tion, my joy and my rest:
He smiles and He loves me and helps me to sing:

I love Thee, I love Thee, and that Thou dost know;
I gaze on my treas - ure and long to be there,
Thy name be my theme, and Thy love be my song;
I'll praise Him, I'll praise Him with notes loud and clear,

But how much I love Thee my ac - tions will show.
With Je - sus and an - gels and kin - dred so dear.
Thy grace shall in - spire both my heart and my tongue.
While riv - ers of pleas - ure my spir - it shall cheer.

There Is a Name I Love to Hear

19

LOBT GOTT, IHR CHRISTEN. C.M.
Nikolaus Herman

Frederick Whitfield, alt.

1. There is a name I love to hear; I love to
2. It tells me of a Sav - iour's love, Who died to
3. Je - sus! the name I love so well, The name I

speak its worth; It sounds like mu - sic in my ear, The
set me free; It tells me of His pre - cious blood, The
love to hear; No saint on earth its worth can tell, No

sweet - est name on earth, The sweet - est name on earth.
blood He shed for me, The blood He shed for me.
heart can know how dear, No heart can know how dear.

20 All Creatures of Our God and King

Francis of Assisi
Tr. by William H. Draper

LASST UNS ERFREUEN. 8.8.4.4.8.8. *with Alleluias*
Melody from "Geistliche Kirchengesange," 1623
Arr. by Max Lyall

1. All crea-tures of our God and King, Lift up your voice and with us
2. Thou rush-ing wind that art so strong, Ye clouds that sail in heaven a-
3. Dear moth-er earth, who day by day Un - fold-est bless-ings on our
4. Let all things their Cre - a - tor bless, And wor-ship Him in hum-ble-

sing Al-le-lu - ia! Al-le - lu - ia! Thou burn-ing sun with gold-en
long, O praise Him! Al-le - lu - ia! Thou ris - ing morn, in praise re-
way, O praise Him! Al-le - lu - ia! The flowers and fruits that in thee
ness, O praise Him! Al-le - lu - ia! Praise, praise the Fa - ther, praise the

beam, Thou sil - ver moon with soft-er gleam! O praise Him, O
joice, Ye lights of eve-ning, find a voice! O praise Him, O
grow, Let them His glo - ry al - so show! O praise Him, O
Son, And praise the Spir-it, Three in One! O praise Him, O

praise Him! Al-le-lu - ia! Al-le-lu - ia! Al-le - lu - ia!
praise Him! Al-le-lu - ia! Al-le-lu - ia! Al-le - lu - ia!
praise Him! Al-le-lu - ia! Al-le-lu - ia! Al-le - lu - ia!
praise Him! Al-le-lu - ia! Al-le-lu - ia! Al-le - lu - ia!

Words used by permission J. Curwen & Sons, Ltd., London.
Arrangement ©Copyright 1963, Broadman Press. All rights reserved. International copyright secured.

Praise Him! Praise Him!

JOYFUL SONG. *Irregular with Refrain*

Fanny J. Crosby

Chester G. Allen

1. Praise Him! praise Him! Je-sus, our bless-ed Re-deem-er! Sing, O Earth, His
2. Praise Him! praise Him! Je-sus, our bless-ed Re-deem-er! For our sins He
3. Praise Him! praise Him! Je-sus, our bless-ed Re-deem-er! Heav'n-ly por-tals

won-der-ful love pro-claim! Hail Him! hail Him! highest archangels in glo-ry;
suff-ered and bled and died; He our Rock, our hope of e-ter-nal sal-va-tion,
loud with ho-san-nas ring! Je-sus, Sav-iour, reigneth for-ev-er and ev-er;

Strength and hon-or give to His ho-ly name! Like a shepherd, Jesus will
Hail Him! hail Him! Je-sus the cru-ci-fied: Sound His prais-es! Jesus who
Crown Him! crown Him! proph-et and priest and king! Christ is com-ing, o-ver the

REFRAIN

guard His children; In His arms He car-ries them all day long:
bore our sor-rows, Love unbound-ed, wonderful, deep and strong: Praise Him! praise Him!
world vic-to-rious, Pow'r and glory un-to the Lord be-long:

tell of His ex-cel-lent great-ness; Praise Him! praise Him! ev-er in joy-ful song!

22 When Morning Gilds the Skies

From the German
Tr. by Edward Caswall

LAUDES DOMINI. 6.6.6.6.6.6.
Joseph Barnby

1. When morn-ing gilds the skies, My heart a-wak-ing cries,
2. When-e'er the sweet church bell Peals o-ver hill and dell,
3. The night be-comes as day, When from the heart we say,
4. In heav'n's e-ter-nal bliss The love-liest strain is this,

May Je-sus Christ be praised! A-like at work and pray'r,
May Je-sus Christ be praised! O hark to what it sings,
May Je-sus Christ be praised! The pow'rs of dark-ness fear,
May Je-sus Christ be praised! Let earth, and sea, and sky

To Je-sus I re-pair; May Je-sus Christ be praised.
As joy-ous-ly it rings, May Je-sus Christ be praised.
When this sweet chant they hear, May Je-sus Christ be praised.
From depth to height re-ply, May Je-sus Christ be praised.

23 Let Us with a Gladsome Mind

MONKLAND. 7.7.7.7.
John Antes
Arr. by John B. Wilkes

John Milton, alt.

1. Let us with a glad-some mind Praise the Lord, for He is kind:
2. He, with all-com-mand-ing might, Filled the new-made world with light:
3. All things liv-ing He doth feed; His full hand sup-plies their need:
4. Let us, then, His praise sing forth, His high maj-es-ty and worth:

For His mer-cies shall en - dure, Ev - er faith - ful, ev - er sure.
For His mer-cies shall en - dure, Ev - er faith - ful, ev - er sure.
For His mer-cies shall en - dure, Ev - er faith - ful, ev - er sure.
For His mer-cies shall en - dure, Ev - er faith - ful, ev - er sure.

Rejoice, Ye Pure in Heart 24

MARION. S.M. *with Refrain*

Edward H. Plumptre

Arthur H. Messiter

1. Re - joice, ye pure in heart, Re - joice, give thanks and sing;
2. Bright youth and snow-crowned age, Strong men and maid - ens fair,
3. Yes, on through life's long path, Still chant - ing as ye go;
4. Still lift your stand - ard high, Still march in firm ar - ray,

Your glo - rious ban-ner wave on high, The cross of Christ your King.
Raise high your free, ex - ult - ing song, God's won - drous praise de - clare.
From youth to age, by night and day, In glad - ness and in woe.
As war-riors thro' the dark - ness toil Till dawns the gold - en day.

REFRAIN

Re - joice, re - joice, Re - joice, give thanks and sing.

25   The Sun Is on the Land and Sea

Louis F. Benson

PARK. 8.4.8.4.8.4.
W. Lawrence Curry

1. The sun is on the land and sea, The day be - gun;
2. Thy love was ev - er in our view, Like stars, by night;
3. We do not know what grief or care The day may bring:

Our morn-ing hymn be - gins with Thee, Blest Three in One;
Thy gifts are ev - 'ry morn-ing new, O God of light;
The heart shall find some glad-ness there That loves its King;

Our praise shall rise con - tin - ual - ly Till day is done.
Thy mer - cy, like the heav-ens' blue, Fills all our sight.
The life that serves Thee ev - 'ry-where Can al - ways sing.

Music from *Hymns for Junior Worship*, Copyright 1940, Presbyterian Board of Christian Education.
Used by permission.

26   O for a Thousand Tongues to Sing

AZMON. C.M.
Carl G. Glaser
Arr. by Lowell Mason

Charles Wesley

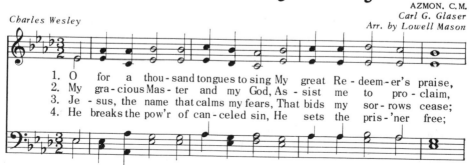

1. O for a thou-sand tongues to sing My great Re - deem-er's praise,
2. My gra-cious Mas - ter and my God, As - sist me to pro - claim,
3. Je - sus, the name that calms my fears, That bids my sor - rows cease;
4. He breaks the pow'r of can-celed sin, He sets the pris - 'ner free;

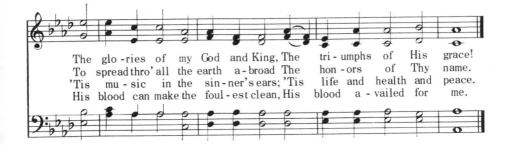

The glo-ries of my God and King, The tri-umphs of His grace!
To spread thro' all the earth a-broad The hon-ors of Thy name.
'Tis mu-sic in the sin-ner's ears; 'Tis life and health and peace.
His blood can make the foul-est clean, His blood a-vailed for me.

Come, Thou Almighty King 27

ITALIAN HYMN (TRINITY). 6.6.4.6.6.6.4.
Felice de Giardini

Anonymous

1. Come, Thou Al-might-y King, Help us Thy name to sing,
2. Come, Thou In-car-nate Word, Gird on Thy might-y sword,
3. Come, Ho-ly Com-fort-er, Thy sa-cred wit-ness bear,
4. To Thee, great One in Three, The high-est prais-es be,

Help us to praise: Fa-ther! all-glo-ri-ous, O'er all vic-to-ri-ous,
Our pray'r at-tend! Come, and Thy peo-ple bless, And give Thy word suc-cess:
In this glad hour! Thou, who al-might-y art, Now rule in ev-'ry heart,
Hence ev-er-more; His sov-'reign maj-es-ty May we in glo-ry see,

Come, and reign o-ver us, An-cient of Days.
Spir-it of ho-li-ness, On us de-scend.
And ne'er from us de-part, Spir-it of pow'r.
And to e-ter-ni-ty Love and a-dore. A-MEN.

28 Crown Him with Many Crowns

Matthew Bridges
Godfrey Thring

DIADEMATA. S.M.D.
George J. Elvey

1. Crown Him with man - y crowns, The Lamb up - on His throne;
2. Crown Him the Lord of life, Who tri - umphed o'er the grave,
3. Crown Him the Lord of peace, Whose pow'r a scep - ter sways
4. Crown Him the Lord of love; Be - hold His hands and side,

Hark! how the heaven - ly an - them drowns All mu - sic but its own:
And rose vic - to - rious in the strife For those He came to save;
From pole to pole, that wars may cease, And all be prayer and praise:
Those wounds, yet vis - i - ble a - bove, In beau - ty glo - ri - fied:

A - wake, my soul, and sing Of Him who died for thee,
His glo - ries now we sing Who died, and rose on high,
His reign shall know no end, And round His pierc - ed feet
All hail, Re - deem - er, hail! For Thou hast died for me:

And hail Him as thy match-less King Through all e - ter - ni - ty.
Who died e - ter - nal life to bring, And lives that death may die.
Fair flowers of par - a - dise ex - tend Their fra - grance ev - er sweet.
Thy praise and glo - ry shall not fail Throughout e - ter - ni - ty.

There Is a Name I Love to Hear

OH, HOW I LOVE JESUS. C.M. *with Refrain*

Frederick Whitfield

Anonymous

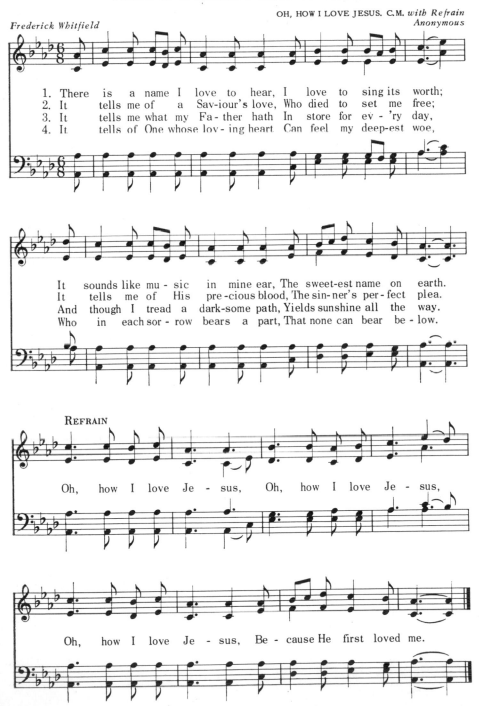

1. There is a name I love to hear, I love to sing its worth;
2. It tells me of a Sav-iour's love, Who died to set me free;
3. It tells me what my Fa-ther hath In store for ev-'ry day,
4. It tells of One whose lov-ing heart Can feel my deep-est woe,

It sounds like mu-sic in mine ear, The sweet-est name on earth.
It tells me of His pre-cious blood, The sin-ner's per-fect plea.
And though I tread a dark-some path, Yields sunshine all the way.
Who in each sor-row bears a part, That none can bear be-low.

REFRAIN

Oh, how I love Je-sus, Oh, how I love Je-sus,

Oh, how I love Je-sus, Be-cause He first loved me.

30

The God of Abraham Praise

Based on the "Yigdal" of Daniel ben Judah
Tr. by Newton Mann and Max Landsberg

LEONI. 6.6.8.4.D.
From a Hebrew Melody
Ad. by Meyer Lyon

1. The God of A-braham praise, All prais-ed be His name,
2. His spir-it flow-eth free, High surg-ing where it will;
3. He hath e-ter-nal life Im-plant-ed in the soul;

Who was, and is, and is to be, And still the same!
In proph-et's word He spoke of old, He speak-eth still.
His love shall be our strength and stay, While a-ges roll.

The one e-ter-nal God, Ere aught that now ap-pears;
Es-tab-lished is His law, And change-less it shall stand,
Praise to the liv-ing God! All prais-ed be His name

The First, the Last: be-yond all thought His time-less years!
Deep writ up-on the hu-man heart, On sea, or land.
Who was, and is, and is to be, And still the same!

At the Name of Jesus

Caroline Noel

HOMAGE. 11.11.11.11.
Austin C. Lovelace

1. At the name of Je - sus ev - 'ry knee shall bow,
2. In your hearts en - throne Him; there let Him sub - due
3. Glo - ry then to Je - sus, who, the Prince of light,

Ev - 'ry tongue con - fess Him King of glo - ry now;
All that is not ho - ly, all that is not true:
To a world in dark - ness brought the gift of sight;

'Tis the Fa - ther's plea - sure we should call Him Lord,
Crown Him as your cap - tain in temp - ta - tion's hour;
Praise to God the Fa - ther; in the Spir - it's love,

Who from the be - gin - ning was the might - y Word.
Let His will en - fold you in its light and pow'r.
Praise we all to - geth - er Him who reigns a - bove.

© Copyright 1964, Broadman Press. All rights reserved. International copyright secured.

32   O Saviour Sweet, O Saviour Kind

Anonymous, st. 1 and 2
Helen A. Dickinson, st. 3

O JESULEIN SUSS. 8.8.8.8.8.8.
Samuel Scheidt's "Tabulaturbuch," 1650
Harm. by Johann Sebastian Bach

1. O Sav - iour sweet, O Sav - iour kind, Thy
2. O Sav - iour sweet, O Sav - iour kind, The
3. O Sav - iour sweet, O Sav - iour kind, Who

Fa - ther's will was in Thy mind When Thou didst
way to please Thee we would find, What - e'er we
came to earth the lost to find, Who died to

come from heav'n to earth, In hu - man form, by
have, it comes of Thee, O let us ev - er
save us on the tree, Our hearts are filled with

hum - ble birth, O Sav - iour sweet, O Sav - iour kind.
near Thee be, O Sav - iour sweet, O Sav - iour kind.
love to Thee, O Sav - iour sweet, O Sav - iour kind.

Stanza 3 Copyright H. W. Gray Co. Used by permission.

O Praise Ye the Lord

Based on Psalm 148 and 150
Henry W. Baker

PHILDON. 10. 10. 11. 11.
Mary E. Caldwell

1. O praise ye the Lord! praise Him in the height; Re-
2. O praise ye the Lord! praise Him up - on earth, In
3. O praise ye the Lord! thanks-giv - ing and song, To

joice in His Word, ye an - gels of light. Ye
tune - ful ac - cord, ye sons of new birth; Praise
Him be out - pour'd all a - ges a - long; For

heav - ens, a - dore Him, by whom ye were made, And
Him who hath brought you His grace from a - bove, Praise
love in cre - a - tion, for heav - en re - stored, For

wor - ship be - fore Him, in bright - ness ar - rayed.
Him who hath taught you to sing of His love.
grace of sal - va - tion, O praise ye the Lord! A - MEN.

© Copyright 1961, 1964, Broadman Press. All rights reserved. International copyright secured.

34 ## O God, Our Help in Ages Past

Isaac Watts

ST. ANNE, C.M.
Probably by William Croft

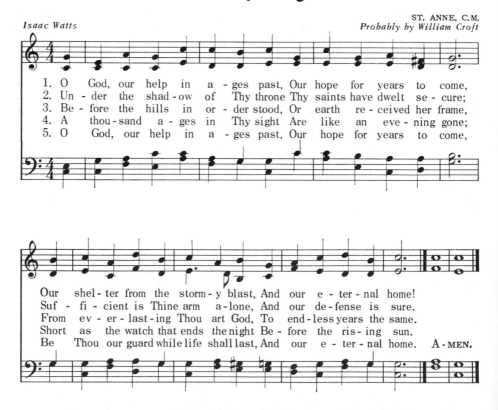

1. O God, our help in a - ges past, Our hope for years to come,
2. Un - der the shad - ow of Thy throne Thy saints have dwelt se - cure;
3. Be - fore the hills in or - der stood, Or earth re - ceived her frame,
4. A thou - sand a - ges in Thy sight Are like an eve - ning gone;
5. O God, our help in a - ges past, Our hope for years to come,

Our shel - ter from the storm - y blast, And our e - ter - nal home!
Suf - fi - cient is Thine arm a - lone, And our de - fense is sure.
From ev - er - last - ing Thou art God, To end - less years the same.
Short as the watch that ends the night Be - fore the ris - ing sun.
Be Thou our guard while life shall last, And our e - ter - nal home. A - MEN.

Praise the Lord, the King of Glory

CHARLES. 8.7.8.7.D.

Delma B. Reno

W. Hines Sims

1. Praise the Lord, the King of glo-ry, Gra-cious Son of God is He;
2. Bless-ed be the King of glo-ry, Sun of right-eous-ness and grace;
3. Might-y is the King of glo-ry, His great works the heav'ns proclaim;

Long fore-told by pro-phets ho-ly, Great in pow'r and maj-es-ty.
Sing, O earth, the won-drous sto-ry; Christ re-deems the fall-en race.
Full of maj-es-ty and ho-ly, Lord of Sab-a-oth His name.

With the Fa-ther through cre-a-tion, Heav'n and earth doth tell His fame;
Praise Him for His great sal-va-tion, Pre-cious Lamb of God a-dore;
Myr-iad tongues in joy-ful cho-rus Sing His praise with sweet-est chords;

Hope and joy of ev-'ry na-tion, Life and light are in His name.
Lord and light of all cre-a-tion, Laud and serve Him ev-er-more.
In our hearts He reign-eth o'er us, King of kings and Lord of lords!

© Copyright 1964, Broadman Press. All rights reserved. International copyright secured.

36 Sing Praise to God Who Reigns Above

Johann J. Schütz
Tr. by Frances E. Cox, alt.

MIT FREUDEN ZART. 8.7.8.7.8.8.7.
Bohemian Brethen's "Kirchengesänge," 1566

1. Sing praise to God who reigns a-bove, The God of all cre - a - tion,
2. What God's al-might-y pow'r hath made, His gra-cious mercy keep - eth;
3. Thus, as I dai-ly walk a-long, I sing a-loud Thy prais - es,

The God of pow'r, the God of love, The God of our sal -
By morn-ing glow or eve-ning shade His watch-ful eye ne'er
That men may hear the grate-ful song My voice un-wea - ried

va - tion; With heal-ing balm my soul He fills, And ev - 'ry faith-less
sleep-eth; With-in the king-dom of His might, Lo! all is just and
rais - es; Be joy-ful in the Lord, my heart, Both soul and bod-y

mur - mur stills: To God all praise and glo - ry.
all is right: To God all praise and glo - ry.
bear your part: To God all praise and glo - ry. A - MEN.

Joyful, Joyful, We Adore Thee

HYMN TO JOY. 8.7.8.7.D.

Henry van Dyke

Arr. from Ludwig van Beethoven

1. Joy - ful, joy - ful, we a - dore Thee, God of glo - ry, Lord of love;
2. All Thy works with joy surround Thee, Earth and heav'n re - flect Thy rays,
3. Thou art giv - ing and for - giv - ing, Ev - er bless - ing, ev - er blest,
4. Mor - tals join the might - y cho - rus Which the morn - ing stars be - gan;

Hearts un - fold like flow'rs be - fore Thee, Open - ing to the sun a - bove.
Stars and an - gels sing a - round Thee, Cen - ter of un - bro - ken praise.
Well - spring of the joy of liv - ing, O - cean - depth of hap - py rest!
Fa - ther - love is reign - ing o'er us, Broth - er - love binds man to man.

Melt the clouds of sin and sad - ness; Drive the dark of doubt a - way;
Field and for - est, vale and moun - tain, Flow - ery mead - ow, flash - ing sea,
Thou our Fa - ther, Christ our Broth - er — All who live in love are Thine;
Ev - er sing - ing, march we on - ward, Vic - tors in the midst of strife;

Giv - er of im - mor - tal glad - ness, Fill us with the light of day!
Chant - ing bird and flow - ing foun - tain Call us to re - joice in Thee.
Teach us how to love each oth - er, Lift us to the joy di - vine.
Joy - ful mu - sic leads us sun - ward In the tri - umph song of life.

Reprinted from *The Poems of Henry van Dyke*, Copyright 1911 Charles Scribner's Sons, 1939 Tertius van Dyke. Used by permission of the publishers.

38 Men and Children Everywhere

ROCK OF AGES, *Irregular*
Ancient Hebrew Melody
Arr. by Max Lyall

John J. Moment

1. Men and chil-dren ev - 'ry-where, With sweet mu - sic fill the air!
2. Morn - ing, eve-ning, bless His name, Skies with crim-son clouds a - flame,
3. Storm and flood and o - cean's roar, Break-ers crash-ing on the shore,

Na - tions, come, your voic - es raise To the Lord in hymns of praise!
Rain-bow arch, His cove-nant sign, Count-less stars by night that shine!
Wa - ter-falls that nev - er sleep, Tow'r-ing moun-tain, can - yon deep,

Join the an - gel song, All the worlds to Him be - long!
Through His far do - main, Love is king where He doth reign!
Tell ye forth His might, Love of life and truth and right!

Ho - ly, ho - ly, To our God all glo - ry be!
Ho - ly, ho - ly, To our God all glo - ry be!
Ho - ly, ho - ly, To our God all glo - ry be!

Words copyright 1930 by the H. W. Gray Co., Inc. Renewed 1958. Used by permission.
Arrangement © Copyright 1964, Broadman Press. All rights reserved. International copyright secured.

ELLACOMBE, C.M.D.

Isaac Watts

From "Gesangbuch der Herzogl," 1784

1. I sing the might-y pow'r of God, That made the moun-tains rise;
2. I sing the good-ness of the Lord, That filled the earth with food;
3. There's not a plant or flow'r be-low, But makes Thy glo-ries known;

That spread the flow-ing seas a-broad, And built the loft-y skies.
He formed the crea-tures with His word, And then pronounced them good.
And clouds a-rise, and tem-pests blow, By or-der from Thy throne;

I sing the wis-dom that or-dained The sun to rule the day;
Lord, how Thy won-ders are dis-played, Wher-e'er I turn my eye,
While all that bor-rows life from Thee Is ev-er in Thy care,

The moon shines full at His com-mand, And all the stars o-bey.
If I sur-vey the ground I tread, Or gaze up-on the sky!
And ev-'ry-where that man can be, Thou, God, art pres-ent there.

40
To God Be the Glory

Fanny J. Crosby

TO GOD BE THE GLORY. 11.11.11.11. *with Refrain*
William H. Doane

1. To God be the glo - ry, great things He hath done; So loved He the
2. O per - fect re - demp - tion, the pur - chase of blood, To ev - 'ry be -
3. Great things He hath taught us, great things He hath done, And great our re -

world that He gave us His Son, Who yield - ed His life an a -
liev - er the prom - ise of God; The - vil - est of - fend - er who
joic - ing thro' Je - sus the Son; But 'pur - er, and high - er and

tone-ment for sin, And o - pened the life-gate that all may go in.
tru - ly be - lieves, That mo-ment from Je - sus a par-don re-ceives.
great-er will be Our won-der, our trans-port, when Je-sus we see.

REFRAIN

Praise the Lord, praise the Lord, Let the earth hear His voice! Praise the Lord,

praise the Lord, Let the peo-ple re - joice! O come to the Fa-ther, thro'

Je-sus the Son, And give Him the glo-ry, great things He hath done.

O Lord, Thou Art My God and King 41

From Psalm 145
"The Psalter," 1912

DUKE STREET. L.M.
John Hatton

1. O Lord, Thou art my God and King, And I will ev-er bless Thy name; I will ex-tol Thee ev-'ry day, And ev-er-more Thy praise pro-claim.

2. The Lord is great-ly to be praised, His great-ness is be-yond our thought, From age to age the sons of men Shall tell the won-ders God has wrought.

3. Up-on Thy glo-rious maj-es-ty And won-drous works my mind shall dwell; Thy deeds shall fill the world with awe, And of Thy great-ness I will tell.

4. Thy match-less good-ness and Thy grace Thy peo-ple shall com-mem-o-rate, And all Thy truth and right-eous-ness My joy-ful song shall cel-e-brate. A-MEN.

42   A Mighty Fortress Is Our God

Martin Luther
Tr. by Frederick H. Hedge

EIN' FESTE BURG. 8.7.8.7.6.6.6.7.
Martin Luther

1. A might-y for-tress is our God, A bul-wark nev-er fail - ing;
2. Did we in our own strength confide, Our striv-ing would be los - ing;

Our help-er He, a - mid the flood Of mor-tal ills pre - vail - ing:
Were not the right Man on our side, The Man of God's own choos - ing:

For still our an - cient foe Doth seek to work us woe; His craft and pow'r are great,
Dost ask who that may be? Christ Je-sus, it is He; Lord Sa - ba - oth, His name,

And, armed with cru - el hate, On earth is not his e - qual.
From age to age the same, And He must win the bat - tle.

God, Who Made the Earth 43

SPRING. *Irregular*
Mrs. S. B. Rhodes
Robert G. McCutchan

1. God, who made the earth, The air, the sky, the sea,
2. God, who made the grass, The flow'r, the fruit, the tree,
3. God, who made the sun, The moon, the stars, is He
4. God, who made all things On earth, in air, in sea,

Who gave the light its birth, Car - eth for me.
The day and night to pass, Car - eth for me.
Who, when life's clouds come on, Car - eth for me.
Who chang - ing sea - sons brings, Car - eth for me.

Copyright 1929. Renewal 1957 in *American Junior Church School Hymnal*. Hope Publishing Co., owner. Used by permission.

44
In Heavenly Love Abiding

NYLAND. 7.6.7.6.D.
Finnish Hymn Melody
Harm. by David Evans

Anna L. Waring

1. In heav'n-ly love a - bid - ing, No change my heart shall fear;
2. Wher - ev - er He may guide me, No want shall turn me back;
3. Green pas - tures are be - fore me, Which yet I have not seen;

And safe is such con - fid - ing, For noth - ing chang-es here:
My Shep-herd is be - side me, And noth - ing can I lack:
Bright skies will soon be o'er me, Where the dark clouds have been:

The storm may roar with - out me, My heart may low be laid;
His wis - dom ev - er wak - eth, His sight is nev - er dim;
My life I can - not meas - ure, The path of life is free;

But God is round a - bout me, And can I be dis - mayed?
He knows the way He tak - eth, And I will walk with Him.
My Sav - iour has my treas - ure, And He will walk with me.

Now, on Land and Sea Descending

VESPER HYMN. 8.7.8.7.8.6.8.7.

Samuel Longfellow

Dimitri S. Bortniansky

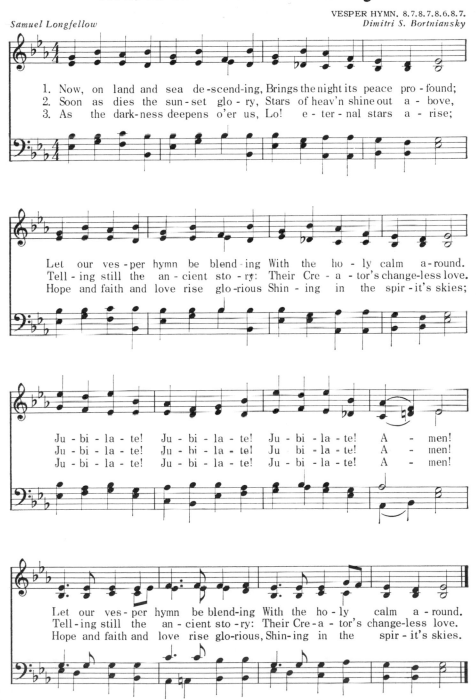

1. Now, on land and sea de-scend-ing, Brings the night its peace pro-found;
2. Soon as dies the sun-set glo-ry, Stars of heav'n shine out a-bove,
3. As the dark-ness deepens o'er us, Lo! e-ter-nal stars a-rise;

Let our ves-per hymn be blend-ing With the ho-ly calm a-round.
Tell-ing still the an-cient sto-ry: Their Cre-a-tor's change-less love.
Hope and faith and love rise glo-rious Shin-ing in the spir-it's skies;

Ju-bi-la-te! Ju-bi-la-te! Ju-bi-la-te! A-men!
Ju-bi-la-te! Ju-bi-la-te! Ju-bi-la-te! A-men!
Ju-bi-la-te! Ju-bi-la-te! Ju-bi-la-te! A-men!

Let our ves-per hymn be blend-ing With the ho-ly calm a-round.
Tell-ing still the an-cient sto-ry: Their Cre-a-tor's change-less love.
Hope and faith and love rise glo-rious, Shin-ing in the spir-it's skies.

Consider the Lilies

BROTHERTON. 11.11.12.11.
Somerset Folk Song

Alice Williams Brotherton

1. Con - sid - er the lil - ies-how state-ly they grow! They toil not, they
2. Con - sid - er the ra - vens-who gives them their food? Who shelters their
3. Our Fa -ther in heav-en, Thy chil-dren on earth, Than lil-ies or

spin not, no seed do they sow; Yet they bloom all the sum - mer, so
nest in the storm-beat- en wood? Who guides the young spar - row? who
ra - vens, Thou hold-est more worth: O guide us and guard us, be

shin-ing and tall, The Fa -ther who loves them takes thought for them all.
watch-es its fall? Their Fa-ther in heav-en takes heed for them all.
near when we call, Up - hold us, en -fold us—we thank Thee for all! A - MEN.

47 Children of the Heavenly Father

Caroline V. Sandell Berg
Tr. by Ernst William Olson

ANNFELT. L.M.
Swedish Melody

1. Chil - dren of the heav'n-ly Fa-ther Safe-ly in His bos - om gath-er;
2. God His own doth tend and nour-ish, In His ho - ly courts they flour-ish.
3. Though He giv-eth or He tak-eth, God His chil-dren ne'er for-sak-eth,

The Lord's My Shepherd   48

Psalm 23
Francis Rous

CRIMOND. C. M.
Jane S. Irvine

49 God of Our Fathers, Whose Almighty Hand

NATIONAL HYMN. 10. 10. 10. 10.

Daniel C. Roberts

George W. Warren

Trumpets before each verse.

1. God of our fa - thers, whose al - might - y
2. Thy love di - vine hath led us in the
3. From war's a - larms, from dead - ly pes - ti -
4. Re - fresh Thy peo - ple on their toil - some

hand Leads forth in beau - ty all the star - ry band
past, In this free land by Thee our lot is cast;
lence, Be Thy strong arm our ev - er sure de - fense;
way, Lead us from night to nev - er - end - ing day;

Of shin - ing worlds in splen - dor through the skies,
Be Thou our rul - er, guard - ian, guide, and stay,
Thy true re - li - gion in our hearts in - crease,
Fill all our lives with love and grace di - vine,

Our grate - ful songs be - fore Thy throne a - rise.
Thy Word our law, Thy paths our cho - sen way.
Thy boun - teous good - ness nour - ish us in peace.
And glo - ry, laud, and praise be ev - er Thine. A - MEN.

There Is a Tender Shepherd 50

GERMAN FOLK TUNE. 7.6.7.6.
German Folk Tune

J. B. Cody

1. There is a ten-der Shep-herd Who watch-es o'er His sheep, And
2. Christ Je-sus is that Shep-herd; Oh, grant, dear Lord, that we With-
3. O bless-ed, ho-ly Je-sus, Thou Shep-herd kind and strong, Thou
4. Our on-ly hope of heav-en, The life, the truth, the way, May

they need fear no e-vil Who in His pas-ture keep.
in Thy pleas-ant pas-tures May safe and hap-py be!
friend so true and lov-ing, May we to Thee be-long!
we, with sins for-giv-en, Praise Thee in end-less lay!

The King of Love My Shepherd Is 51

DOMINUS REGIT ME. 8.7.8.7.
John B. Dykes

Henry W. Baker

1. The King of love my Shep-herd is, Whose good-ness fail-eth nev-er;
2. Where streams of liv-ing wa-ter flow, My ran-somed soul He lead-eth,
3. Per-verse and fool-ish, oft I strayed, But yet in love He sought me,
4. In death's dark vale I fear no ill With Thee, dear Lord, be-side me;
5. And so through all the length of days Thy good-ness faileth nev-er:

I noth-ing lack if I am His And He is mine for-ev-er.
And, where the ver-dant pas-tures grow, With food ce-les-tial feed-eth.
And on His shoul-der gen-tly laid, And home, re-joic-ing, brought me.
Thy rod and staff my com-fort still, Thy cross be-fore to guide me.
Good Shepherd, may I sing Thy praise With-in Thy house for-ev-er. A-MEN.

52   God Who Touchest Earth with Beauty

Mary S. Edgar

GENEVA. 8. 5. 8. 5.
C. Harold Lowden

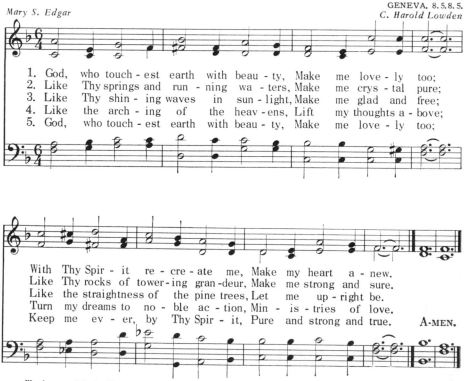

1. God, who touch - est earth with beau - ty, Make me love - ly too;
2. Like Thy springs and run - ning wa - ters, Make me crys - tal pure;
3. Like Thy shin - ing waves in sun - light, Make me glad and free;
4. Like the arch - ing of the heav - ens, Lift my thoughts a - bove;
5. God, who touch - est earth with beau - ty, Make me love - ly too;

With Thy Spir - it re - cre - ate me, Make my heart a - new.
Like Thy rocks of tow - er - ing gran - deur, Make me strong and sure.
Like the straight - ness of the pine trees, Let me up - right be.
Turn my dreams to no - ble ac - tion, Min - is - tries of love.
Keep me ev - er, by Thy Spir - it, Pure and strong and true.

A-MEN.

Words copyright by Mary S. Edgar. Used by permission.
Music copyright by C. Harold Lowden. Used by permission.

This Is My Father's World

2 stanzas

TERRA PATRIS. S. M. D.
Franklin L. Sheppard

Maltbie D. Babcock

1. This is my Fa-ther's world, And to my lis-t'ning ears, All
2. This is my Fa-ther's world, The birds their car-ols raise; The
3. This is my Fa-ther's world, O let me ne'er for-get That

na-ture sings, and round me rings The mu-sic of the spheres.
morn-ing light, the lil-y white De-clare their Ma-ker's praise.
though the wrong seems oft so strong, God is the Rul-er yet.

This is my Fa-ther's world, I rest me in the thought Of
This is my Fa-ther's world, He shines in all that's fair; In the
This is my Fa-ther's world, The bat-tle is not done; Je-

rocks and trees, of skies and seas; His hand the won-ders wrought.
rus-tling grass I hear Him pass, He speaks to me ev-'ry-where.
sus who died shall be sat-is-fied, And earth and heav-en be one.

54   God of the Earth, the Sky, the Sea

Samuel Longfellow

HARPETH. L.M.
Carlton R. Young

1. God of the earth, the sky, the sea,
2. Thy love is in the sun - shine's glow,
3. We feel Thy calm at eve - ning's hour,

Mak - er of all a - bove, be - low,
Thy life is in the quick - 'ning air,
Thy gran - deur in the march of night,

Cre - a - tion lives and moves in Thee;
When light - nings flash and storm - winds blow,
And when the morn - ing breaks in pow'r,

Thy pres - ent life through all doth flow.
There is Thy pow'r, Thy law is there.
We hear Thy word, "Let there be light!"

Music © Copyright 1964, Broadman Press. All rights reserved. International copyright secured.

All Things Bright and Beautiful

SPOHR. 7.6.7.6. D.

Cecil F. Alexander

Ad. from Louis Spohr

1. All things bright and beau - ti - ful, All things great and small,
2. Pur - ple - head - ed moun - tain, Riv - er run - ning by,
3. Cold wind in the win - ter, Pleas - ant sum - mer sun,

All things wise and won - der - ful; Our Fa - ther made them all.
Sun - set and the morn - ing That bright - ens up the sky:
Ripe fruits in the gar - den; He made them ev - 'ry one.

Each lit - tle flow'r that o - pens, Each lit - tle bird that sings;
The tall trees in the green-wood, The mead - ows for our play,
He gave us eyes to see them, And lips that we might tell

He made their glow - ing col - ors, He made their ti - ny wings.
The rush - es by the wa - ter To gath - er ev - 'ry day.
How good is God our Fa - ther Who do - eth all things well.

56   For the Beauty of the Earth

DIX. 7.7.7.7.7.7.
From a Chorale by Conrad Kocher

Folliott S. Pierpoint

1. For the beau - ty of the earth, For the glo - ry
2. For the won - der of each hour Of the day and
3. For the joy of hu - man love, Broth - er, sis - ter,
4. For Thy church that ev - er - more Lift - eth ho - ly

of the skies, For the love which from our birth
of the night, Hill and vale, and tree and flow'r,
par - ent, child, Friends on earth, and friends a - bove,
hands a - bove, Of - f'ring up on ev - 'ry shore

O - ver and a - round us lies; Christ our God, to
Sun and moon, and stars of light; Christ our God, to
For all gen - tle thoughts and mild; Christ our God, to
Her pure sac - ri - fice of love; Christ our God, to

Thee we raise This our hymn of grate - ful praise.
Thee we raise This our hymn of grate - ful praise.
Thee we raise This our hymn of grate - ful praise.
Thee we raise This our hymn of grate - ful praise. A-MEN.

Away in a Manger

57

MUELLER. 11.11.11.11.
James R. Murray

Anonymous

1. A - way in a man - ger, no crib for a bed, The lit - tle Lord Je - sus laid down His sweet head; The stars in the sky looked down where He lay, The lit - tle Lord Je - sus, a - sleep on the hay.
2. The cat - tle are low - ing, the Ba - by a - wakes, But lit - tle Lord Je - sus, no cry - ing He makes; I love Thee, Lord Je - sus! look down from the sky, And stay by my cra - dle till morn - ing is nigh.
3. Be near me, Lord Je - sus, I ask Thee to stay Close by me for- ev - er, and love me, I pray; Bless all the dear chil - dren in Thy ten - der care, And fit us for heav - en to live with Thee there. A - MEN.

REPEAT

58 Oh, Come, All Ye Children

Christian v. Schmid
Tr., Anonymous

IHR KINDERLEIN, KOMMET. 11.11.11.11.
Johann A. P. Schulz

1. Oh, come, all ye chil - dren, oh, come, one and all,
2. He's born in a sta - ble for you and for me,
3. Dear Christ Child, what gifts can we chil - dren be - stow
4. Our hearts, then, to Thee we will of - fer to - day,

To Beth - le - hem haste, to the man - ger so small,
Draw near by the bright gleam-ing star - light to see,
By which our af - fec - tion and glad - ness to show?
We of - fer them glad - ly, ac - cept them, we pray,

God's Son for a gift has been sent you this
In swad - dling clothes ly - ing, so meek and so
No rich - es and treas - ures of val - ue can
And make them so spot - less and pure that we

night To be your Re - deem - er, your joy and de - light.
mild, And pur - er than an - gels, the heav - en - ly Child.
be, But hearts that be - lieve are ac - cept - ed by Thee.
may A - bide in Thy pres - ence in heav - en for aye.

Silent Night, Holy Night

Joseph Mohr
Tr. by John Freeman Young, st. 1 and 3
Anonymous, st. 2 and 4

STILLE NACHT. *Irregular*
Franz Gruber

1. Si - lent night, ho - ly night, All is calm, all is bright
2. Si - lent night, ho - ly night, Dark - ness flies, all is light;
3. Si - lent night, ho - ly night, Son of God, love's pure light
4. Si - lent night, ho - ly night, Won - drous Star, lend thy light;

Round yon Vir - gin Moth - er and child! Ho - ly In - fant so
Shep - herds hear the an - gels sing, "Al - le - lu - ia!
Ra - diant beams from Thy ho - ly face, With the dawn of re -
With the an - gels let us sing, Al - le - lu - ia

ten - der and mild, Sleep in heav - en - ly
hail the King! Christ the Sav - iour is
deem - ing grace, Je - sus, Lord, at Thy
to our King; Christ the Sav - iour is

peace, Sleep in heav - en - ly peace.
born, Christ the Sav - iour is born."
birth, Je - sus, Lord, at Thy birth.
born, Christ the Sav - iour is born.

60

The First Noel the Angel Did Say

THE FIRST NOEL. *Irregular with Refrain*
Traditional Melody from
W. Sandys' "Christmas Carols," 1833

Old English Carol

1. The first No-el the an-gel did say, Was to cer-tain poor
2. They look-ed up and saw a star Shin-ing in the
3. And by the light of that same star Three Wise Men
4. Then let us all with one ac-cord Sing prais-es

shepherds in fields as they lay; In fields where they lay keeping their
east, be-yond them far, And to the earth it gave great
came from coun - try far; To seek for a king was their in-
to our heav-en - ly Lord Who hath made heav'n and earth of

REFRAIN

sheep, On a cold win-ter's night that was so deep.
light, And so it con-tinued both day and night. No - el, No - el,
tent, And to fol - low the star wher-ev - er it went.
naught, And with His blood man-kind hath bought.

No - el, No - el, Born is the King of Is - ra - el.

Angels We Have Heard on High

GLORIA. 7.7.7.7. *with Refrain*
Old French Carol
Arr. by Warren M. Angell

Traditional

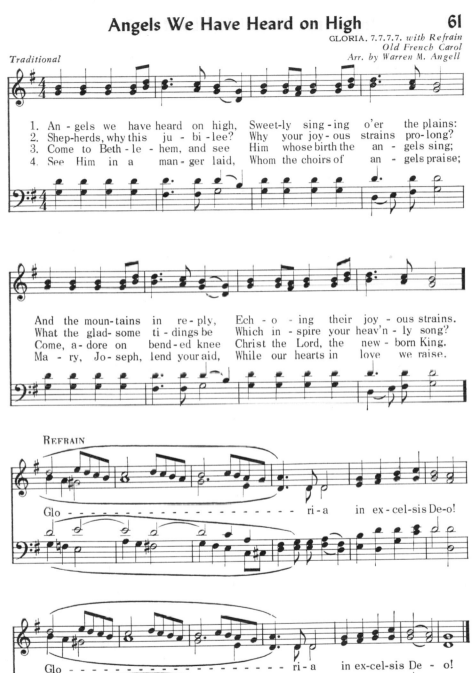

1. An - gels we have heard on high, Sweet-ly sing-ing o'er the plains:
2. Shep-herds, why this ju - bi - lee? Why your joy-ous strains pro-long?
3. Come to Beth - le - hem, and see Him whose birth the an - gels sing;
4. See Him in a man-ger laid, Whom the choirs of an - gels praise;

And the moun-tains in re-ply, Ech - o - ing their joy - ous strains.
What the glad-some ti - dings be Which in - spire your heav'n - ly song?
Come, a - dore on bend-ed knee Christ the Lord, the new - born King.
Ma - ry, Jo - seph, lend your aid, While our hearts in love we raise.

REFRAIN

Glo - - - - - - - - - - - - - - - ri - a in ex - cel-sis De-o!

Glo - - - - - - - - - - - - - - - ri - a in ex-cel-sis De - o!

62 Joy to the World! The Lord Is Come

From Psalm 98
Isaac Watts

ANTIOCH. C.M.
Arr. from George F. Handel

1. Joy to the world! the Lord is come; Let earth re - ceive her King;
2. Joy to the earth! the Sav - iour reigns; Let men their songs em - ploy;
3. No more let sins and sor - rows grow, Nor thorns in - fest the ground;
4. He rules the world with truth and grace, And makes the na - tions prove

Let ev - 'ry heart pre - pare Him room,
While fields and floods, rocks, hills, and plains
He comes to make His bless - ings flow
The glo - ries of His right - eous - ness,

And heav'n and na - ture sing, And heav'n and na - ture sing,
Re - peat the sound-ing joy, Re - peat the sound-ing joy,
Far as the curse is found, Far as the curse is found,
And won - ders of His love, And won - ders of His love,

And heav'n, and heav'n and na - ture sing.
Re - peat, re - peat the sound - ing joy.
Far as, far as the curse is found.
And won - ders, won - ders of His love.

O Little Town of Bethlehem

63

ST. LOUIS. 8.6.8.6.7.6.8.6.

Phillips Brooks

Lewis H. Redner

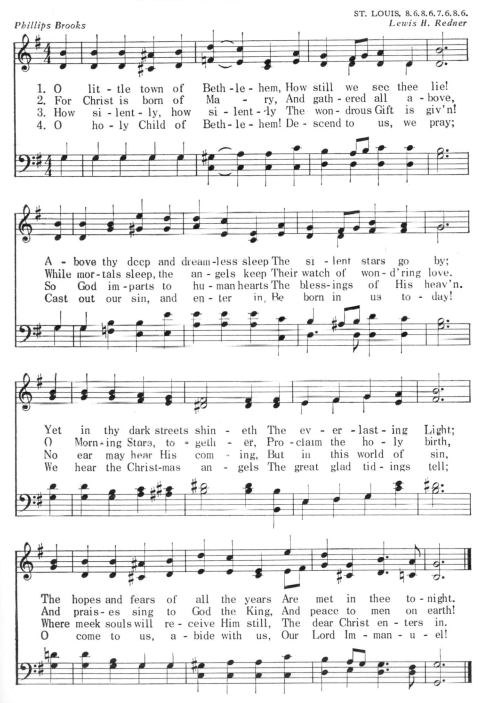

1. O lit - tle town of Beth - le - hem, How still we see thee lie!
2. For Christ is born of Ma - ry, And gath - ered all a - bove,
3. How si - lent - ly, how si - lent - ly The won - drous Gift is giv'n!
4. O ho - ly Child of Beth - le - hem! De - scend to us, we pray;

A - bove thy deep and dream-less sleep The si - lent stars go by;
While mor-tals sleep, the an - gels keep Their watch of won-d'ring love.
So God im-parts to hu - man hearts The bless-ings of His heav'n.
Cast out our sin, and en - ter in, Be born in us to - day!

Yet in thy dark streets shin - eth The ev - er - last - ing Light;
O Morn-ing Stars, to - geth - er, Pro - claim the ho - ly birth,
No ear may hear His com - ing, But in this world of sin,
We hear the Christ-mas an - gels The great glad tid - ings tell;

The hopes and fears of all the years Are met in thee to - night.
And prais - es sing to God the King, And peace to men on earth!
Where meek souls will re - ceive Him still, The dear Christ en - ters in.
O come to us, a - bide with us, Our Lord Im - man - u - el!

64 What Child Is This

William C. Dix

GREENSLEEVES. 8.7.8.7. *with Refrain*
Sixteenth Century English Melody

1. What Child is this, who, laid to rest, On Ma-ry's lap is sleep-ing?
2. So bring Him in-cense, gold, and myrrh, Come, peas-ant, king, to own Him;

Whom an-gels greet with an-thems sweet, While shepherds watch are keep-ing?
The King of kings sal-va-tion brings, Let lov-ing hearts en-throne Him.

REFRAIN

This, this is Christ the King, Whom shep-herds guard and an-gels sing:

Haste, haste to bring Him laud, The Babe, the Son of Ma-ry.

O Come, O Come, Emmanuel

From the Latin, 12 century
Tr. J.M. Neale, st. 1
Tr. H.S. Coffin, st. 2, Anon., st. 3

VENI EMMANUEL. 8.8.8.8.8.8.
Ancient Plain Song, 13th Century

1. O come, O come, Em-man - u - el, And ran - som cap - tive
2. O come, Thou Wis - dom from on high, And or - der all things,
3. O come, Thou Bright and Morn - ing Star, And bring us com - fort

Is - ra - el, That mourns in lone - ly ex - ile here
far and nigh; To us the path of knowl - edge show,
from a - far! Dis - pel the shad - ows of the night

Un - til the Son of God ap - pear. Re-joice! Re-joice! Em-
And cause us in Thy ways to go. Re-joice! Re-joice! Em-
And turn our dark - ness in - to light. Re-joice! Re-joice! Em-

man - u - el Shall come to thee, O Is - ra - el!
man - u - el Shall come to thee, O Is - ra - el!
man - u - el Shall come to thee, O Is - ra - el!

66 Gentle Mary Laid Her Child

TEMPUS ADEST FLORIDUM. 7.6.7.6.D.
A Spring Carol, c. Fourteenth Century
Arr. by Ernest MacMillan

Joseph Simpson Cook

1. Gen - tle Ma - ry laid her Child Low - ly in a man - ger;
2. An - gels sang a - bout His birth; Wise Men sought and found Him;
3. Gen - tle Ma - ry laid her Child Low - ly in a man - ger;

There He lay, the un - de - filed, To the world a stran - ger:
Heav - en's star shone bright-ly forth, Glo - ry all a - round Him:
He is still the un - de - filed, But no more a stran - ger:

Such a Babe in such a place, Can He be the Sav - iour?
Shep-herds saw the won-drous sight, Heard the an - gels sing - ing;
Son of God, of hum - ble birth, Beau - ti - ful the sto - ry;

Ask the saved of all the race Who have found His fa - vor.
All the plains were lit that night, All the hills were ring - ing.
Praise His name in all the earth, Hail the King of glo - ry!

Words used by permission of Gordon V. Thompson, Limited, Toronto, Canada, owners of the copyright.
Music used by permission of Ernest MacMillan.

Good Christian Men, Rejoice

Medieval Latin Carol
Tr. by John M. Neale

IN DULCI JUBILO, *Irregular*
Fourteenth Century German Melody

1. Good Chris-tian men, re-joice With heart and soul and voice!
2. Good Chris-tian men, re-joice With heart and soul and voice!
3. Good Chris-tian men, re-joice With heart and soul and voice!

Give ye heed to what we say: Je-sus Christ is born to-day.
Now ye hear of end-less bliss: Je-sus Christ was born for this.
Now ye need not fear the grave: Je-sus Christ was born to save;

Man and beast be-fore Him bow, And He is in the man-ger now:
He hath o-pened heav-en's door, And man is bless'd for-ev-er-more.
Calls you one, and calls you all, To gain His ev-er-last-ing hall.

Christ is born to-day, Christ is born to-day!
Christ was born for this, Christ was born for this!
Christ was born to save, Christ was born to save!

68 As with Gladness Men of Old

DIX. 7.7.7.7.7.7.

William C. Dix

Abridged from a Chorale by Conrad Kocher

1. As with glad-ness men of old Did the guid-ing
2. As with joy-ous steps they sped To that low-ly
3. As they of-fered gifts most rare At that man-ger

star be-hold; As with joy they hailed its light,
man-ger bed, There to bend the knee be-fore
rude and bare, So may we with ho-ly joy,

Lead-ing on-ward, beam-ing bright; So, most gra-cious
Him whom heav'n and earth a-dore; So may we with
Pure and free from sin's al-loy, All our cost-liest

Lord, may we Ev-er-more be led to Thee.
will-ing feet Ev-er seek Thy mer-cy seat.
treas-ures bring, Christ, to Thee, our heav'n-ly King. A-MEN.

O Come, All Ye Faithful

John F. Wade
Tr. by Frederick Oakeley

ADESTE FIDELES. *Irregular with Refrain*
John F. Wade

1. O come, all ye faith-ful, joy-ful and tri-um-phant, O come ye, O
2. Sing, choirs of an-gels, sing in ex-ul-ta-tion, O sing, all ye
3. Yea, Lord, we greet Thee, born this hap-py morn-ing, Je - sus, to

come ye to Beth - le - hem! Come and be-hold Him, born the King of
bright hosts of heav'n a - bove! Glo - ry to God, all glo - ry in the
Thee be all glo - ry giv'n, Word of the Fa - ther, now in flesh ap-

REFRAIN

an - gels!
high- est! O come, let us a - dore Him, O come, let us a - dore Him,
pear- ing!

O come, let us a - dore Him, Christ the Lord!

70 Sing Hosannas

MCCRAY. 10.6.10.6. *with Refrain*
Polish Carol
Arr. by Alta C. Faircloth

Alta C. Faircloth

1. Hark to the sto-ry an-gels are tell-ing Of the birth of Je-sus,
2. Shep-herds a-keep-ing watch on the hill-side, Heard the won-drous sto-ry,
3. Come, all ye peo-ple, come to the man-ger, Wor-ship and a-dore Him;

Born in a man-ger mid cat-tle low-ly Is the Babe most ho-ly.
Knelt down in won-der, gazed at the glo-ry Sud-den-ly ap-pear-ing.
Sing as the an-gels, kneel as the shep-herds, To the Christ, our Sav-iour.

REFRAIN

Sing, all ye an-gels! Sing, all ye shep-herds! Sing to the

lit-tle Babe in the man-ger, Sing a soft ho-san-na,

Sing a loud ho-san-na, Je-sus Christ is born to-day.

© Copyright 1959, 1964, Broadman Press. All rights reserved. International copyright secured.

Hark! The Herald Angels Sing

MENDELSSOHN. 7.7.7.7.D. *with Refrain*

Charles Wesley
Alt. by George Whitefield

Felix Mendelssohn
Ad. by William H. Cummings

1. Hark! the her - ald an - gels sing, "Glo - ry to the new - born King;
2. Christ, by high - est heav'n a - dored, Christ, the ev - er - last - ing Lord:
3. Hail the heav'n - born Prince of Peace! Hail the Sun of right - eous - ness!

Peace on earth, and mer - cy mild; God and sin - ners rec - on - ciled."
Late in time, be - hold Him come, Off - spring of a vir - gin's womb.
Light and life to all He brings, Ris'n with heal - ing in His wings.

Joy - ful, all ye na - tions, rise, Join the tri - umph of the skies;
Veiled in flesh the God-head see, Hail th'in - car - nate De - i - ty!
Mild He lays His glo - ry by, Born that man no more may die,

With an - gel - ic hosts pro - claim, "Christ is born in Beth - le - hem!"
Pleased as man with men to dwell, Je - sus our Im - man - u - el.
Born to raise the sons of earth, Born to give them sec - ond birth.

Hark! the her - ald an - gels sing, "Glo - ry to the new - born King."

72

Infant Holy, Infant Lowly

Polish Carol
Para. by Edith M.G. Reed

W ZLOBIE LEZY. *Irregular*
Polish Carol
Harm. by David H. Jones

1. In - fant ho - ly, In - fant low - ly, For His
2. Flocks were sleep - ing; Shep - herds keep - ing Vig - il

bed a cat - tle stall; Ox - en low - ing, Lit - tle
till the morn - ing new Saw the glo - ry, Heard the

know - ing Christ the Babe is Lord of all. Swift are
sto - ry, Ti - dings of a gos - pel true. Thus re -

wing - ing An - gels sing - ing, No - els ring - ing, Ti - dings
joic - ing, Free from sor - row, Prais - es voic - ing Greet the

bring - ing: Christ the Babe is Lord of all.
mor - row: Christ the Babe was born for you.

Words from *Kingsway Carol Book.* Used by permission of the publishers, Evans Brothers, Ltd.
Music from *The Hymnbook.* © Copyright 1955 by John Ribble. Used by permission.

Once in Royal David's City

IRBY. *Irregular*
Henry J. Gauntlett

Cecil F. Alexander, alt.

1. Once in roy - al Da - vid's cit - y Stood a
2. He came down to earth from heav - en, Who is
3. And our eyes at last shall see Him, Through His
4. Not in that poor low - ly sta - ble, With the

low - ly cat - tle shed, Where a moth - er laid her
God and Lord of all; And His shel - ter was a
own re-deem - ing love; For that Child so dear and
ox - en stand - ing by, We shall see Him, but in

Ba - by In a man - ger for His bed: Ma - ry
sta - ble, And His cra - dle was a stall: Ma - ry
gen - tle Is our Lord in heav'n a - bove: Ma - ry
heav - en, Set at God's right hand on high: Ma - ry

was that moth - er mild, Je - sus Christ her lit - tle Child.
was that moth - er mild, Je - sus Christ her lit - tle Child.
was that moth - er mild, Je - sus Christ her lit - tle Child.
was that moth - er mild, Je - sus Christ her lit - tle Child.

74   Angels, from the Realms of Glory

James Montgomery

REGENT SQUARE. 8.7.8.7.8.7.
Henry Smart

1. An - gels, from the realms of glo - ry, Wing your flight o'er
2. Shep - herds, in the fields a - bid - ing, Watch - ing o'er your
3. Sag - es, leave your con - tem -pla - tions,Bright - er vi - sions
4. Saints, be - fore the al - tar bend - ing, Watch - ing long in

all the earth; Ye who sang cre - a -tion's sto - ry,
flocks by night, God with man is now re - sid - ing,
beam a - far; Seek the great De - sire of na - tions,
hope and fear, Sud - den - ly the Lord, de - scend - ing,

Now pro - claim Mes - si - ah's birth: Come and wor - ship,
Yon - der shines the in - fant Light: Come and wor - ship,
Ye have seen His na - tal star: Come and wor - ship,
In His tem - ple shall ap - pear: Come and wor - ship,

come and wor - ship, Wor - ship Christ, the new - born King!
come and wor - ship, Wor - ship Christ, the new - born King!
come and wor - ship, Wor - ship Christ, the new - born King!
come and wor - ship, Wor - ship Christ, the new - born King!

There's a Song in the Air

CHRISTMAS SONG. 6.6.6.6.12.12.

Josiah G. Holland

Karl P. Harrington

1. There's a song in the air! There's a star in the sky!
2. There's a tu - mult of joy O'er the won - der - ful birth,
3. In the light of that star Lie the a - ges im - pearled;
4. We re - joice in the light And we ech - o the song

There's a moth - er's deep prayer And a ba - by's low cry!
For the Vir - gin's sweet boy Is the Lord of the earth.
And that song from a - far Has swept o - ver the world.
That comes down thro' the night From the heav - en - ly throng.

And the star rains its fire while the beau - ti - ful sing,
Ay! the star rains its fire while the beau - ti - ful sing,
Ev - 'ry hearth is a - flame, and the beau - ti - ful sing
Ay! we shout to the love - ly e - van - gel they bring,

For the man - ger of Beth - le - hem cra - dles a King!
For the man - ger of Beth - le - hem cra - dles a King!
In the homes of the na - tions that Je - sus is King!
And we greet in His cra - dle our Sav - iour and King!

76 Thou Didst Leave Thy Throne

Emily E. S. Elliott

MARGARET, *Irregular*
Timothy R. Matthews

1. Thou didst leave Thy throne And Thy king-ly crown, When Thou
2. Heav-en's arch-es rang When the an-gels sang, Pro-
3. The fox-es found rest, And the birds their nest In the
4. Thou cam-est, O Lord, With the liv-ing word That should
5. When the heav-ens shall ring, And the an-gels sing, At Thy

cam-est to earth for me; But in Beth-le-hem's home
claim-ing Thy roy-al de-gree; But of low-ly birth
shade of the for-est tree; But Thy couch was the sod,
set Thy peo-ple free; But with mock-ing scorn,
com-ing to vic-to-ry, Let Thy voice call me home,

Was there found no room For Thy ho-ly na-tiv-i-ty.
Didst Thou come to earth, And in great hu-mil-i-ty.
O Thou Son of God, In the des-erts of Gal-i-lee.
And with crown of thorn, They bore Thee to Cal-va-ry.
Say-ing, "Yet there is room, There is room at My side for thee."

REFRAIN

1-4. O come to my heart, Lord Je-sus, There is room in my heart for Thee.
5. My heart shall re-joice, Lord Je-sus, When Thou com-est and call-est for me.

Jesus Was a Loving Teacher

77

BROCKLESBURY. 8.7.8.7.

Wilhelmina D'A. Stephens

Charlotte A. Barnard

1. Je - sus was a lov - ing Teach-er, Help-ing peo-ple day by day
2. Je - sus was a pa - tient Teach-er, Want-ing all to learn God's will,
3. God, we thank Thee for this Teach-er, And our praise to Thee we give,

Know the love of God our Fa - ther, Teach-ing them to love and pray.
Tell - ing sto - ries they'd re - mem - ber—Sto - ries that we're read-ing still.
For His love and for His pa-tience, Show - ing peo - ple how to live.

Words ©Copyright 1946 by The Westminster Press; from *Songs and Hymns for Primary Children*.
Used by permission.

Oh, Sing a Song of Bethlehem

KINGSFOLD. C.M.D.
English Traditional Melody
Arr. by Ralph Vaughan Williams

Louis F. Benson

1. Oh, sing a song of Beth-le-hem, Of shep-herds watch-ing there,
2. Oh, sing a song of Naz-a-reth, Of sun-ny days of joy,
3. Oh, sing a song of Gal-i-lee, Of lake and woods and hill,

And of the news that came to them From an-gels in the air.
Oh, sing of fra-grant flow-ers' breath And of the sin-less Boy;
Of Him who walked up-on the sea And bade its waves be still;

The light that shone on Beth-le-hem Fills all the world to-day;
For now the flow'rs of Naz-a-reth In ev-'ry heart may grow;
For though like waves on Gal-i-lee, Dark seas of trou-ble roll,

Of Je-sus' birth and peace on earth The an-gels sing al-way.
Now spreads the fame of His dear name On all the winds that blow.
When faith has heard the Mas-ter's word, Falls peace up-on the soul.

Tell Me the Stories of Jesus

STORIES OF JESUS. 8.4.8.4.5.4.5.4.

William H. Parker

Frederic A. Challinor

1. Tell me the sto-ries of Je - sus I love to hear;
   Things I would ask Him to tell me If He were here;
   Scenes by the way - side, Tales of the sea,
   Sto - ries of Je - sus, Tell them to me.

2. First let me hear how the chil - dren Stood round His knee;
   And I shall fan - cy His bless - ing Rest - ing on me;
   Words full of kind - ness, Deeds full of grace,
   All in the love - light Of Je - sus' face.

3. In - to the ci - ty I'd fol - low The chil-dren's band,
   Wav - ing a branch of a palm tree High in my hand;
   One of His her - alds, Yes, I would sing
   Loud - est ho - san - nas, "Je - sus is King!"

Used by permission of the National Sunday School Union.

Hosanna, Loud Hosanna

Jeannette Threlfall

ELLACOMBE. 7.6.7.6.D.
From "Gesangbuch der Herzogl," 1784

1. Ho - san - na, loud ho - san - na The lit - tle chil - dren sang;
2. From Ol - i - vet they fol - lowed 'Mid an ex - ult - ant crowd,
3. "Ho - san - na in the high - est!" That an - cient song we sing,

Through pil - lared court and tem - ple The love - ly an - them rang;
The vic - tor palm branch wav - ing, And chant - ing clear and loud;
For Christ is our Re - deem - er, The Lord of heav'n, our King.

To Je - sus, who had blessed them Close fold - ed to His breast,
The Lord of men and an - gels Rode on in low - ly state,
O may we ev - er praise Him With heart and life and voice,

The chil - dren sang their prais - es, The sim - plest and the best.
Nor scorned that lit - tle chil - dren Should on His bid - ding wait.
And in His bliss - ful pres - ence E - ter - nal - ly re - joice!

Tell Me the Story of Jesus

STORY OF JESUS. 8.7.8.7.D. *with Refrain*

Fanny J. Crosby

John R. Sweney

1. Tell me the sto - ry of Je - sus, Write on my heart ev - 'ry word;
2. Fast - ing a - lone in the des - ert, Tell of the days that are past,
3. Tell of the cross where they nailed Him, Writhing in an - guish and pain;

REFRAIN—*Tell me the sto - ry of Je - sus, Write on my heart ev - 'ry word;*

FINE.

Tell me the sto - ry most pre - cious, Sweetest that ev - er was heard.
How for our sins He was tempt - ed, Yet was tri - um - phant at last.
Tell of the grave where they laid Him, Tell how He liv - eth a - gain.

Tell me the sto - ry most pre - cious, Sweetest that ev - er was heard.

Tell how the an - gels, in cho - rus, Sang as they wel comed His birth,
Tell of the years of His la - bor, Tell of the sor - row He bore,
Love in that sto - ry so ten - der, Clear - er than ev - er I see:

D.C. *for Refrain*

"Glo - ry to God in the high - est! Peace and good ti - dings to earth."
He was de - spised and af - flict - ed, Home - less, re - ject - ed, and poor.
Stay, let me weep while you whis - per, Love paid the ran - som for me.

82. Thy Works of Love

Calvin W. Laufer

DUNDEE, C.M.
"Scottish Psalter," 1615

1. Thy works of love and friend-ship, Lord, Help us to think of Thee;
2. They bring to mind the qui-et scene When chil-dren climbed Thy knee,
3. In vil-lage, mar-ket place, and throng, The chil-dren cheered Thy days;
4. We love Thee for Thy works di-vine, Still more for what Thou art;

Thy heal-ing won-ders and Thy Word Re-call fair Gal-i-lee.
And when Thou saidst with friend-ly mien, "Let them come un-to Me."
And in the Tem-ple court their song To Thee was per-fect praise.
And that our lives may be like Thine, We give Thee, Lord, our heart.

Words © Copyright 1927 by C. W. Laufer; renewed 1955 by E. B. Laufer; from *Hymns for Junior Worship.*
Used by permission.

83. My Master Was So Very Poor

Harry Lee

DUNWODY, L.M.
Alta C. Faircloth

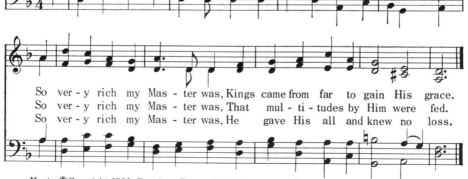

1. My Mas-ter was so ver-y poor, A man-ger was His cra-dling place;
2. My Mas-ter was so ver-y poor, And with the poor He broke the bread;
3. My Mas-ter was so ver-y poor, They nailed Him nak-ed to a cross;

So ver-y rich my Mas-ter was, Kings came from far to gain His grace.
So ver-y rich my Mas-ter was, That mul-ti-tudes by Him were fed.
So ver-y rich my Mas-ter was, He gave His all and knew no loss.

Music © Copyright 1964, Broadman Press. All rights reserved. International copyright secured.

Ask Ye What Great Thing I Know 84

Johann C. Schwedler
Tr. by Benjamin H. Kennedy

HENDON. 7.7.7.7.7.
Henri A. C. Malan

1. Ask ye what great thing I know That delights and
2. What is faith's foundation strong? What awakes my
3. This is that great thing I know; This delights and

stirs me so? What the high reward I win? Whose the name I
lips to song? He who bore my sinful load, Purchased for me
stirs me so; Faith in Him who died to save, Him who triumphed

glory in? Jesus Christ, the crucified.
peace with God, Jesus Christ, the crucified.
o'er the grave, Jesus Christ, the crucified.

85   Ride On! Ride On in Majesty!

Henry H. Milman

TRURO. L.M.
From Thomas Williams'
"Psalmodia Evangelica," 1789

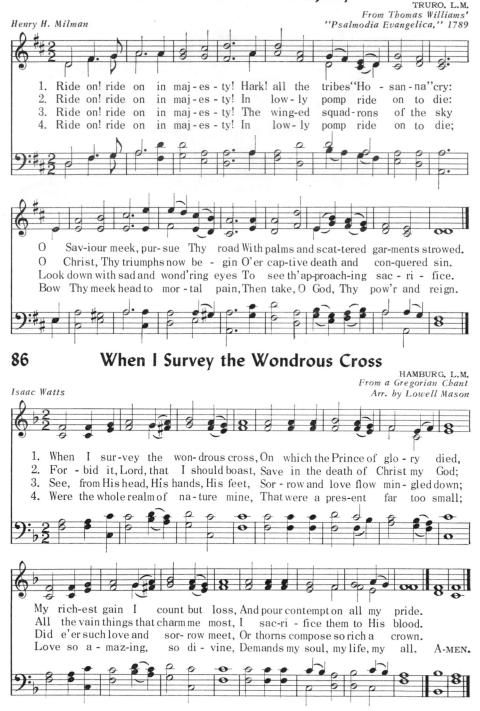

1. Ride on! ride on in maj-es-ty! Hark! all the tribes "Ho-san-na" cry:
2. Ride on! ride on in maj-es-ty! In low-ly pomp ride on to die:
3. Ride on! ride on in maj-es-ty! The wing-ed squad-rons of the sky
4. Ride on! ride on in maj-es-ty! In low-ly pomp ride on to die;

O   Sav-iour meek, pur-sue Thy road With palms and scat-tered gar-ments strowed.
O   Christ, Thy triumphs now be-gin O'er cap-tive death and con-quered sin.
Look down with sad and wond'ring eyes To see th'ap-proach-ing sac-ri-fice.
Bow Thy meek head to mor-tal pain, Then take, O God, Thy pow'r and reign.

86   When I Survey the Wondrous Cross

Isaac Watts

HAMBURG. L.M.
From a Gregorian Chant
Arr. by Lowell Mason

1. When I sur-vey the won-drous cross, On which the Prince of glo-ry died,
2. For-bid it, Lord, that I should boast, Save in the death of Christ my God;
3. See, from His head, His hands, His feet, Sor-row and love flow min-gled down;
4. Were the whole realm of na-ture mine, That were a pres-ent far too small;

My rich-est gain I count but loss, And pour contempt on all my pride.
All the vain things that charm me most, I sac-ri-fice them to His blood.
Did e'er such love and sor-row meet, Or thorns compose so rich a crown.
Love so a-maz-ing, so di-vine, Demands my soul, my life, my all.   A-MEN.

Into the Woods My Master Went

Sidney Lanier

LANIER. *Irregular*
Peter C. Lutkin

1. In - to the woods my Mas - ter went, Clean for-spent, for - spent;
2. Out of the woods my Mas - ter went, And He was well con - tent:

In - to the woods my Mas - ter came, For - spent with love and shame. But the
Out of the woods my Mas - ter came, Con - tent with death and shame, When

ol - ives they were not blind to Him, The lit - tle gray leaves were kind to Him,
death and shame would woo Him last, From un - der the trees they drew Him last,

The thorn tree had a mind to Him, When in - to the woods He came.
'Twas on a tree they slew Him last, When out of the woods He came. A-MEN.

There Is a Green Hill Far Away

GREEN HILL. C.M. *with Refrain*

Cecil F. Alexander

George C. Stebbins

1. There is a green hill far a-way, With-out a cit-y wall,
2. We may not know, we can-not tell What pains He had to bear;
3. He died that we might be for-giv'n, He died to make us good,
4. There was no oth-er good e-nough To pay the price of sin,

Where the dear Lord was cru-ci-fied, Who died to save us all.
But we be-lieve it was for us He hung and suf-fered there.
That we might go at last to heav'n, Saved by His pre-cious blood.
He on-ly could un-lock the gate Of heav'n, and let us in.

REFRAIN

Oh, dear-ly, dear-ly has He loved, And we must love Him, too,

And trust in His re-deem-ing blood, And try His works to do.

I Know that My Redeemer Lives 89

DUKE STREET. L.M.
John Hatton

Samuel Medley

1. I know that my Re - deem - er lives; What com-fort
2. He lives tri - um phant from the grave, He lives e -
3. He lives and grants me dai - ly breath; He lives, and
4. He lives, all glo - ry to His name! He lives, my

this sweet sen - tence gives! He lives, He lives, who once was dead;
ter - nal - ly to save, He lives all - glo - rious in the sky,
I shall con - quer death; He lives my man - sion to pre - pare,
Je - sus, still the same. Oh, the sweet joy this sen - tence gives,

He lives, my ev - er - liv - ing head.
He lives ex - alt - ed there on high.
He lives to bring me safe - ly there.
"I know that my Re - deem - er lives!"

Good Christian Men, Rejoice and Sing!

VULPIUS. 8.8.8.4.

Melody by Melchior Vulpius
Arr. by Max Lyall

C. A. Alington

1. Good Chris - tian men, re - joice and sing!
2. The Lord of life is ris'n for aye;
3. Praise we in songs of vic - to - ry
4. Thy name we bless, O ris - en Lord,

Now is the tri - umph of your King!
Bring flow'rs of joy to strew His way;
That love, that life which can - not die,
And sing to - day with one ac - cord

To all the world glad news we bring:
Let all man - kind re - joice and say:
And sing with hearts up - lift - ed high:
The life laid down, the life re - stored:

Hal - le - lu - jah, hal - le - lu - jah, hal - le - lu - jah!
Hal - le - lu - jah, hal - le - lu - jah, hal - le - lu - jah!
Hal - le - lu - jah, hal - le - lu - jah, hal - le - lu - jah!
Hal - le - lu - jah, hal - le - lu - jah, hal - le - lu - jah!

Text from *Hymns Ancient and Modern.* **Used by permission of William Clowes and Sons, Ltd., London.**
Arrangement © Copyright 1964, Broadman Press. All rights reserved. International copyright secured.

Christ the Lord Is Risen Today

EASTER HYMN. 7.7.7.7. *with Alleluias*
From *"Lyra Davidica,"* 1708

Charles Wesley

1. Christ the Lord is ris'n to - day, Al - - - - le - lu - ia!
2. Lives a - gain our glo - rious King, Al - - - - le - lu - ia!
3. Love's re - deem - ing work is done, Al - - - - le - lu - ia!
4. Soar we now where Christ has led, Al - - - - le - lu - ia!

Sons of men and an - gels say, Al - - - - le - lu - ia!
Where, O Death, is now thy sting? Al - - - - le - lu - ia!
Fought the fight, the bat - tle won, Al - - - - le - lu - ia!
Fol - lowing our ex - alt - ed Head, Al - - - - le - lu - ia!

Raise your joys and tri - umphs high, Al - - - le - lu - ia!
Dy - ing once He all doth save, Al - - - le - lu - ia!
Death in vain for - bids Him rise, Al - - - le - lu - ia!
Made like Him, like Him we rise, Al - - - le - lu - ia!

Sing, ye heav'ns, and earth, re - ply, Al - le - lu - ia!
Where thy vic - to - ry, O Grave? Al - le - lu - ia!
Christ hath o - pened Par - a - dise, Al - le - lu - ia!
Ours the cross, the grave, the skies, Al - le - lu - ia!

O Joyous Easter Morning

MEIRIONYDD. 7.6.7.6.D.
Welsh Hymn Melody

Anonymous

1. O joy - ous East - er morn - ing, That saw the Lord a - rise!
2. O glad - some East - er morn - ing, Our hearts re - joice to - day,

O bright and hap - py morn - ing! The clouds have left the skies.
The grave and death are con - quered, He is of life the way.

The night of grief is end - ed, The day has come a - gain,
The hosts of sin are van - quished, He is the vic - tor, King;

And Christ has won the vic - t'ry, For all the sons of men.
Then let us all with glad - ness Our thank - ful prais - es sing.

We Welcome Glad Easter

JOANNA. 11. 11. 11. 11.
Welsh Hymn Melody

Anonymous

1. We wel - come glad East - er when Je - sus a - rose,
2. And tell how the wo - men came ear - ly that day,
3. And sing of the an - gel who said: "Do not fear!
4. And think of the prom - ise which Je - sus did give:

And won a great vic - to - ry o - ver His foes.
And there at the tomb found the stone rolled a - way.
Your Sav - iour is ris'n a - gain; He is not here."
"That he who be - lieves in Me al - so shall live!"

REFRAIN

Then raise your glad voi - ces, ye Chris - tians, and sing,

Bring sweet East - er prais - es to Je - sus our King.

94   The First Lord's Day

William N. McElrath

SPRINGBROOK. C.M. *with Refrain*
William N. McElrath

1. They rolled a stone be-fore the door, As in the grave He lay;
2. The birds that sang, the flow'rs that bloomed, They brought no joy that spring,
3. All earth is dressed in green this day, To greet our ris-en Lord;

God raised Him up, our liv-ing Lord, And made the first Lord's Day.
Till Christ was raised from death to be Our liv-ing Lord and King.
We praise Him, for He lives a-gain, He keeps His prom-ised word.

REFRAIN

We sing for joy, we sing for joy, With lov-ing thanks we say:

"God raised Him up, our liv-ing Lord, And made the first Lord's Day."

© Copyright 1964, Broadman Press. All rights reserved. International copyright secured.

Come, Ye Faithful, Raise the Strain

John of Damascus
Tr. by John M. Neale

ST. KEVIN. 7.6.7.6.D.
Arthur S. Sullivan

1. Come, ye faith-ful, raise the strain Of tri - um - phant glad - ness:
2. 'Tis the spring of souls to - day: Christ hath burst His pris - on,
3. "Al - le - lu - ia!" now we cry To our King im - mor - tal,

God hath brought His peo - ple forth In - to joy from sad - ness:
From the frost and gloom of death Light and life have ris - en:
Who, tri - um - phant, burst the bars Of the tomb's dark por - tal:

Now re - joice, Je - ru - sa - lem, And with true af - fec - tion
All the win - ter of our sins, Long and dark, is fly - ing
"Al - le - lu - ia!" with the Son, God the Fa - ther prais - ing;

Wel - come in un - wea - ried strains Je - sus' res - ur - rec - tion.
From His light, to whom we give Thanks and praise un - dy - ing.
"Al - le - lu - ia!" yet a - gain To the Spir - it rais - ing.

Rejoice, the Lord Is King

Charles Wesley

DARWALL. 6.6.6.6.8.8.
John Darwall

1. Re - joice, the Lord is King: Your Lord and King a - dore!
2. Je - sus, the Sav - iour, reigns, The God of truth and love;
3. His king-dom can - not fail, He rules o'er earth and heav'n;

Re - joice, give thanks and sing, And tri - umph
When He had purged our stains, He took His
The keys of death and hell Are to our

ev - er - more: Lift up your heart, lift up your voice!
seat a - bove: Lift up your heart, lift up your voice!
Je - sus giv'n: Lift up your heart, lift up your voice!

Re - joice, a - gain I say, re - joice!
Re - joice, a - gain I say, re - joice!
Re - joice, a - gain I say, re - joice! A - MEN.

The King Shall Come When Morning Dawns 97

AZMON C.M.

From the Greek
Tr. by John Brownlie

Carl G. Glaser
Arr. by Lowell Mason

1. The King shall come when morn-ing dawns, And light tri - um - phant breaks;
2. Not, as of old, a lit - tle child To bear, and fight, and die,
3. The King shall come when morn-ing dawns, And light and beau - ty brings;

When beau - ty gilds the east - ern hills, And life to joy a - wakes.
But crowned with glo - ry like the sun, That lights the morn - ing sky.
Hail! Christ the Lord; Thy peo - ple pray, Come quick - ly, King of kings.

98 I Know Whom I Have Believed

Daniel W. Whittle

EL NATHAN. C.M. *with Refrain*
James McGranahan

1. I know not why God's won-drous grace To me He hath made known,
2. I know not how this sav-ing faith To me He did im-part,
3. I know not how the Spir-it moves, Con-vinc-ing men of sin,
4. I know not when my Lord may come, At night or noon-day fair,

Nor why, un-wor-thy, Christ in love Re-deemed me for His own.
Nor how be-liev-ing in His Word Wrought peace with-in my heart.
Re-veal-ing Je-sus thro' the Word, Cre-at-ing faith in Him.
Nor if I'll walk the vale with Him, Or meet Him in the air.

REFRAIN

But "I know whom I have be-liev-ed, and am per-suad-ed that He is

a-ble To keep that which I've com-mit-ted Un-to Him a-gainst that day."

Songs of Praise the Angels Sang

James Montgomery, alt.

INNOCENTS, 7,7,7,7.
From "The Parish Choir," 1850

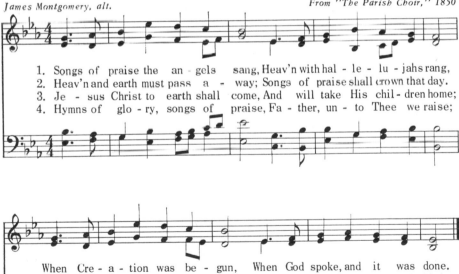

1. Songs of praise the an - gels sang, Heav'n with hal - le - lu - jahs rang,
2. Heav'n and earth must pass a - way; Songs of praise shall crown that day.
3. Je - sus Christ to earth shall come, And will take His chil - dren home;
4. Hymns of glo - ry, songs of praise, Fa - ther, un - to Thee we raise;

When Cre - a - tion was be - gun, When God spoke, and it was done.
God will make new heav'ns, new earth; Songs of praise shall hail their birth.
Un - til then, with heart and voice, We shall praise Him and re - joice.
Learn - ing here by faith and love, Songs of praise to sing a - bove.

100 **Spirit Divine, Attend Our Prayer**

Andrew Reed
Ad. by Samuel Longfellow

GRÄFENBERG. C.M.
From Johann Crüger's
"Praxis Pietatis Melica," 1653

1. Spir - it di - vine, at - tend our pray'r, And make our heart Thy home;
2. Come as the light! to us re - veal The truth we long to know;
3. Come as the fire and purge our hearts Like sac - ri - fi - cial flame,

De - scend with all Thy gra - cious pow'r; Come, Ho - ly Spir - it, come.
Re - veal the nar - row path of right, The way of du - ty show.
Till our whole souls an of - f'ring be In love's re - deem - ing name. A - MEN.

Come, Holy Spirit, Come

Dorothy A. Thrupp

FRANCONIA. 6.6.8.6.
Konig's "Harmonischer Liederschatz," 1738

1. Come, Ho-ly Spir-it, come; Oh, hear my hum-ble pray'r! Stoop
2. Thy light, Thy love im-part, And let it ev-er be A
3. Let Thy rich grace in-crease, Through all my earth-ly days, The

down and make my heart Thy home, And shed Thy bless-ing there.
ho-ly, hum-ble, hap-py heart, A dwell-ing place for Thee.
fruits of right-eous-ness and peace, To Thine e-ter-nal praise.

Holy Spirit, Hear Us

William H. Parker

ERNSTEIN. 6.5.6.5.
James F. Swift

1. Ho-ly Spir-it, hear us; Help us while we sing;
2. Ho-ly Spir-it, prompt us When we kneel to pray;
3. Ho-ly Spir-it, shine Thou On the Book we read;
4. Ho-ly Spir-it, give us Each a seek-ing mind;

Breathe in-to the mu-sic Of the praise we bring.
Near-er come and teach us What we ought to say.
Gild its ho-ly pag-es With the light we need.
Make us more like Je-sus, Gen-tle, pure, and kind. A-MEN.

Words copyright. Used by permission of The National Sunday School Union.
Music copyright. Used by permission of the Methodist Youth Department.

103 Breathe on Me, Breath of God

TRENTHAM. S.M.
Robert Jackson

Edwin Hatch

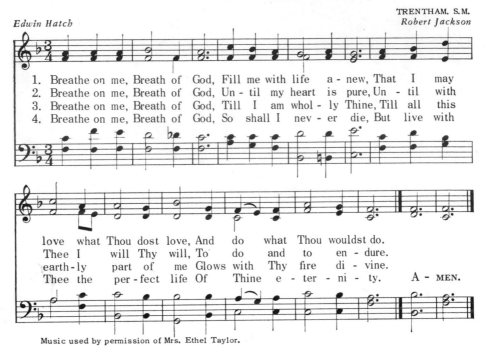

1. Breathe on me, Breath of God, Fill me with life a-new, That I may
2. Breathe on me, Breath of God, Un-til my heart is pure, Un-til with
3. Breathe on me, Breath of God, Till I am whol-ly Thine, Till all this
4. Breathe on me, Breath of God, So shall I nev-er die, But live with

love what Thou dost love, And do what Thou wouldst do.
Thee I will Thy will, To do and to en-dure.
earth-ly part of me Glows with Thy fire di-vine.
Thee the per-fect life Of Thine e-ter-ni-ty. A-MEN.

Music used by permission of Mrs. Ethel Taylor.

104 Holy Spirit, Hear Us

From the German by Joseph Mohr
Tr. by Claudia F. Hernaman

CASWALL. 6.5.6.5.
Friedrich Filitz

1. Ho-ly Spir-it, hear us On this sa-cred day;
2. Come as once Thou cam-est To the faith-ful few
3. Light-en Thou our dark-ness, Be Thy-self our Light;
4. Ho-ly Spir-it, hear us On this sa-cred day;

Come to us with bless-ing, Come with us to stay.
Pa-tient-ly a-wait-ing Je-sus' prom-ise true.
Strengthen Thou our weak-ness, Spir-it of all might.
Come to us with bless-ing, Come with us to stay.

My Bible! 'Tis a Book Divine

105

ANGELUS. L.M.
"Heilige Seelenlust," 1657

Anonymous

1. My Bi - ble! 'tis a book di - vine, Where heav'n - ly truth and mer - cy shine, And wis - dom speaks in ev - 'ry line, And speaks to me, and speaks to me.

2. My Bi - ble! in this book a - lone I find God's ho - ly will made known; And here His love to man is shown, His love to me, His love to me.

3. My Bi - ble! here with joy I trace The rec - ords of re - deem - ing grace; Glad ti - dings to a sin - ful race, Good news to me, good news to me.

4. My Bi - ble! here it is I read How Je - sus did for sin - ners bleed. Oh, this was won - drous love in - deed: Christ died for me, Christ died for me!

106   Break Thou the Bread of Life

Mary A. Lathbury, st. 1 and 2
Alexander Groves, st. 3 and 4

BREAD OF LIFE. 6.4.6.4.D.
William F. Sherwin

1. Break Thou the bread of life, Dear Lord, to me,
2. Bless Thou the truth, dear Lord, To me, to me,
3. Thou art the bread of life, O Lord, to me,
4. O send Thy Spir - it, Lord, Now un - to me,

As Thou didst break the loaves Be - side the sea;
As Thou didst bless the bread By Gal - i - lee;
Thy ho - ly Word the truth That sav - eth me;
That He may touch mine eyes, And make me see:

Be - yond the sa - cred page I seek Thee, Lord;
Then shall all bond - age cease, All fet - ters fall;
Give me to eat and live With Thee a - bove;
Show me the truth con - cealed With - in Thy Word,

My spir - it pants for Thee, O liv - ing Word.
And I shall find my peace, My all in all.
Teach me to love Thy truth, For Thou art love.
And in Thy Book re - vealed I see the Lord. A - MEN.

Holy Bible, Book Divine

John Burton, Sr.

ALETTA. 7.7.7.7.
William B. Bradbury

1. Ho - ly Bi - ble, Book di - vine,
2. Mine to chide me when I rove,
3. Mine to com - fort in dis - tress,
4. Mine to tell of joys to come,

Pre - cious treas - ure, thou art mine:
Mine to show a Sav - iour's love;
Suf - fering in this wil - der - ness;
And the reb - el sin - ner's doom:

Mine to tell me whence I came;
Mine thou art to guide and guard;
Mine to show, by liv - ing faith,
O thou ho - ly Book di - vine,

Mine to teach me what I am.
Mine to pun - ish or re - ward.
Man can tri - umph o - ver death.
Pre - cious treas - ure, thou art mine.

108 The Bible Is a Treasure Book

CAMPMEETING. C.M.
Early American Melody
Harm. by Robert G. McCutchan

Elizabeth McE. Shields

1. The Bi-ble is a treas-ure book Of sto-ries that are true:
2. The Bi-ble is a treas-ure book Of ver-ses old and new:
3. The Bi-ble is a treas-ure book: It tells how, long a-go,

It tells of peo-ple long a-go—Of folks like me and you.
Some make us think of love-ly things; Some show us what to do.
Christ Je-sus came to live on earth, Our Fa-ther's love to show.

Words Copyright 1944, by Elizabeth McE. Shields. Used by permission.

109 Father of Mercies, in Thy Word

GRÄFENBERG. C.M.
From Johann Cruger's
"Praxis Pietatis Melica," 1653

Anne Steele

1. Fa-ther of mer-cies, in Thy Word What end-less glo-ry shines!
2. Oh, may these heav'n-ly pag-es be My ev-er dear de-light,
3. Di-vine In-struct-or, gra-cious Lord, Be Thou for-ev-er near;

For-ev-er be Thy Name a-dored For these ce-les-tial lines.
And still new beau-ties may I see, And still in-creas-ing light.
Teach me to love Thy sa-cred Word, And find my Sav-iour there. A-MEN.

The Heavens Declare Thy Glory 110

DUKE STREET. L.M.
John Hatton

Isaac Watts

1. The heav'ns declare Thy glo - ry, Lord, In ev-'ry star Thy wisdom shines;
2. The roll-ing sun, the chang-ing light, And nights and days Thy pow'r confess;
3. Great Sun of Right-eous-ness, a - rise, Bless the dark world with heav'nly light;
4. Thy no-blest won-ders here we view In souls renewed, and sins forgiv'n;

But when our eyes be - hold Thy Word, We read Thy name in fair-er lines.
But the blest Vol-ume Thou hast writ Re - veals Thy jus - tice and Thy grace.
Thy gos-pel makes the sim-ple wise, Thy laws are pure, Thy judgment right.
Lord, cleanse my sins, my soul re - new, And make Thy Word my guide to heav'n.

Spread, O Spread, Thou Mighty Word 111

Jonathan Friedrich Bohnmaier
Tr. by Catherine Winkworth

GOTT SEI DANK. 7.7.7.7.
Freylinghausen's "Gesangbuch," 1704

1. Spread, O spread, thou might-y word, Spread the king-dom of the Lord,
2. Word of how the Fa-ther's will Made the world, and keeps it, still;
3. Word of life, most pure and strong, Word for which the na-tions long,

That to earth's re-mot-est bound Men may heed the joy-ful sound;
How His on-ly Son He gave, Man from sin and death to save;
Spread a-broad, un-til from night All the world a-wakes to light.

112 O Word of God Incarnate

MUNICH. 7.6.7.6.D.
"Neuvermehrtes Meiningisches Gesangbuch," 1693
Arr. by Felix Mendelssohn

William W. How

1. O Word of God In - car - nate, O Wis - dom from on high,
2. The church from Thee, her Mas - ter, Re - ceived the gift di - vine,
3. It float - eth like a ban - ner Be - fore God's host un - furled;
4. O make Thy church, dear Sav - iour, A lamp of pur - est gold,

O Truth un - changed, un - chang - ing, O Light of our dark sky:
And still that light she lift - eth O'er all the earth to shine:
It shin - eth like a bea - con A - bove the dark - ling world:
To bear be - fore the na - tions Thy true light as of old:

We praise Thee for the ra - diance That from the hal - lowed page,
It is the sa - cred cas - ket, Where gems of truth are stored;
It is the chart and com - pass That o'er life's surg - ing sea,
O teach Thy wan - d'ring pil - grims By this their path to trace,

A lan - tern to our foot - steps, Shines on from age to age.
It is the heav'n - drawn pic - ture Of Thee, the liv - ing Word.
'Mid mists and rocks and quick - sands, Still guides, O Christ, to Thee.
Till, clouds and dark - ness end - ed, They see Thee face to face. A-MEN.

Thy Word Is Like a Garden, Lord

113

CLONMEL. C. M. D.
Irish Melody
Arr. by William J. Reynolds

Edwin Hodder

1. Thy Word is like a gar - den, Lord, With flow - ers bright and fair;
2. Thy Word is like a star - ry host; A thou - sand rays of light

And ev - 'ry one who seeks may pluck A love - ly clus - ter there.
Are seen to guide the trav - el - er And make his path - way bright.

Thy Word is like a deep, deep mine; And jew - els rich and rare
O may I love Thy pre - cious Word, May I ex - plore the mine,

Are hid - den in its might - y depths For ev - 'ry search - er there.
May I the fra - grant flow - ers glean, May light up - on me shine. A - MEN.

Arrangement ©Copyright 1952, Broadman Press. All rights reserved. International copyright secured.

114   # Take My Life, and Let It Be

Frances R. Havergal

HENDON. 7.7.7.7.7.
Henri A. Cesar Malan

1. Take my life and let it be Con-se-crat-ed,
2. Take my feet and let them be Swift and beau-ti-
3. Take my sil-ver and my gold, Not a mite would
4. Take my will and make it Thine, It shall be no

Lord, to Thee; Take my hands and let them move At the im-pulse
ful for Thee; Take my voice and let me sing Al-ways, on-ly,
I with-hold; Take my mo-ments and my days, Let them flow in
long-er mine; Take my heart, it is Thine own, It shall be Thy

of Thy love, At the im-pulse of Thy love.
for my King, Al-ways, on-ly, for my King.
cease-less praise, Let them flow in cease-less praise.
roy-al throne, It shall be Thy roy-al throne. A-MEN.

Touch Me, Lord Jesus

RIDGECREST. 5.5.6.5. *with Refrain*
B. B. McKinney

Louise Creamer

1. Touch me, Lord Je - sus, With Thy love di - vine; Cleanse my heart, dear
2. Touch me, Lord Je - sus, Calm the fears in me; Let me know Thy
3. Touch me, Lord Je - sus, With Thy pow'r di - vine; Make each throb-bing
4. Touch me, Lord Je - sus, Make my heart Thy throne;Mold my life and

REFRAIN

Mas - ter, Make me whol - ly Thine.
pres - ence In each soul I see.
heart-beat Sing in tune with Thine. Touch me, bless-ed Je - sus,
use me Ev - er as Thine own.

I would be Thine own; Take my will for - ev - er, Make it Thine a - lone.

Copyright 1940 by The Sunday School Board of the Southern Baptist Convention. All rights reserved.

116

Just As I Am, Thine Own to Be

Marianne Hearn

JUST AS I AM. 8.8.8.6.
Joseph Barnby

1. Just as I am, Thine own to be, Friend of the young, who lov-est me,
2. In the glad morn-ing of my day, My life to give, my vows to pay,
3. I would live ev - er in the light; I would work ev - er for the right;
4. Just as I am, young, strong, and free, To be the best that I can be

To con - se - crate my - self to Thee, O Je - sus Christ, I come.
With no re - serve and no de - lay, With all my heart I come.
I would serve Thee with all my might; There - fore, to Thee I come.
For truth, and right-eous-ness, and Thee, Lord of my life, I come.

117

Just As I Am

Charlotte Elliott

WOODWORTH. L.M.
William B. Bradbury

1. Just as I am, with-out one plea, But that Thy blood was shed for me,
2. Just as I am, and wait-ing not To rid my soul of one dark blot,
3. Just as I am, Thou wilt re-ceive, Wilt wel-come, pardon, cleanse, relieve,
4. Just as I am, Thy love un-known Hath bro-ken ev-'ry bar-rier down;

And that Thou bidd'st me come to Thee, O Lamb of God, I come! I come!
To Thee whose blood can cleanse each spot, O Lamb of God, I come! I come!
Be - cause Thy prom-ise I be-lieve, O Lamb of God, I come! I come!
Now to be Thine, yea, Thine a-lone, O Lamb of God, I come! I come!

Only Trust Him

STOCKTON. C.M. *with Refrain*
John H. Stockton

John H. Stockton

1. Come, ev-'ry soul by sin op-pressed, There's mer-cy with the Lord,
2. For Je-sus shed His pre-cious blood Rich bless-ings to be-stow;
3. Yes, Je-sus is the truth, the way, That leads you in-to rest;
4. Come, then, and join this ho-ly band, And on to glo-ry go,

And He will sure-ly give you rest By trust-ing in His word.
Plunge now in-to the crim-son flood That wash-es white as snow.
Be-lieve in Him with-out de-lay, And you are ful-ly blest.
To dwell in that ce-les-tial land, Where joys im-mor-tal flow.

REFRAIN

On-ly trust Him, on-ly trust Him, on-ly trust Him now;

He will save you, He will save you, He will save you now.

DEDICATION

119   Dear Lord, We Give Our Youth to Thee

LOYALTY. C.M.
Roberta Bitgood

Calvin W. Laufer

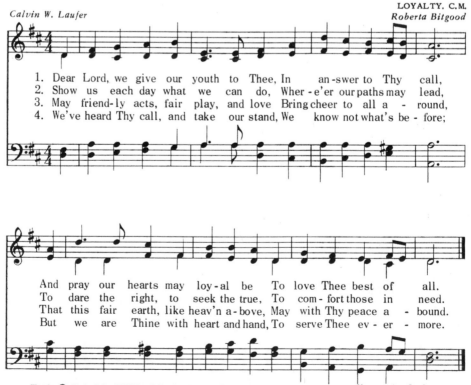

1. Dear Lord, we give our youth to Thee, In an-swer to Thy call,
2. Show us each day what we can do, Wher-e'er our paths may lead,
3. May friend-ly acts, fair play, and love Bring cheer to all a - round,
4. We've heard Thy call, and take our stand, We know not what's be - fore;

And pray our hearts may loy-al be To love Thee best of all.
To dare the right, to seek the true, To com-fort those in need.
That this fair earth, like heav'n a-bove, May with Thy peace a - bound.
But we are Thine with heart and hand, To serve Thee ev - er - more.

Words © Copyright 1927 by C. W. Laufer; renewed 1955 by E. B. Laufer; from *Hymns for Junior Worship*. Used by permission. Music © Copyright 1964, Broadman Press. All rights reserved. International copyright secured.

I Am Thine, O Lord

I AM THINE. 10.7.10.7. *with Refrain*

120

Fanny J. Crosby

William H. Doane

1. I am Thine, O Lord, I have heard Thy voice, And it told Thy
2. Con - se - crate me now to Thy serv - ice, Lord, By the pow'r of
3. O the pure de - light of a sin - gle hour That be - fore Thy

love to me; But I long to rise in the arms of faith, And be
grace di - vine; Let my soul look up with a stead-fast hope, And my
throne I spend; When I kneel in pray'r, and with Thee, my God, I com-

REFRAIN

clos - er drawn to Thee.
will be lost in Thine. Draw me near - er, near-er, bless-ed
mune as friend with friend!

Lord, To the cross where Thou hast died; Draw me near - er, near - er,

near - er, bless- ed Lord, To Thy pre - cious, bleed - ing side.

"Are Ye Able," Said the Master

121

BEACON HILL. 8.7.8.7. *with Refrain*

Earl Marlatt

Harry S. Mason

1. "Are ye a - ble," said the Mas - ter, "To be cru - ci - fied with Me?"
2. "Are ye a - ble?" still the Mas - ter Whis-pers down e - ter - ni - ty,

"Yea," the stur - dy dream - ers an - swered, "To the death we fol - low Thee."
And he - ro - ic spir - its an - swer, Now, as then in Gal - i - lee,

REFRAIN

"Lord, we are a - ble," our spir - its are Thine, Re - mold them,

make us like Thee, di - vine: Thy guid - ing ra - diance a - bove

us shall be A bea - con to God, to faith and loy - al - ty.

Living for Jesus

LIVING. 10. 10. 10. 10. *with Refrain*

Thomas O. Chisholm

C. Harold Lowden

1. Liv-ing for Je-sus a life that is true, Striv-ing to please Him in all that I do,
2. Liv-ing for Je-sus who died in my place, Bearing on Calv'ry my sin and disgrace,
3. Liv-ing for Jesus thro' earth's little while, My dearest treasure, the light of His smile,

Yielding al-le-giance, glad-hearted and free, This is the pathway of blessing for me.
Such love constrains me to answer His call, Follow His lead-ing and give Him my all.
Seeking the lost ones He died to re-deem, Bringing the wea-ry to find rest in Him.

REFRAIN

O Je-sus, Lord and Sav-iour, I give my-self to Thee; For Thou, in Thine a-tone-ment, Didst give Thy-self for me; I own no oth-er Mas-ter, My heart shall be Thy throne; My life I give, henceforth to live, O Christ, for Thee a-lone.

Copyright 1945. Renewal. The Rodeheaver Company, owner. All rights reserved. Used by permission.

123 Give of Your Best to the Master

BARNARD. 8.7.8.7.D. *with Refrain*

Howard B. Grose

Charlotte A. Barnard

1. Give of your best to the Mas-ter, Give of the strength of your youth;
2. Give of your best to the Mas-ter, Give Him first place in your heart;
3. Give of your best to the Mas-ter, Naught else is wor-thy His love;

Throw your soul's fresh, glowing ar-dor In-to the bat-tle for truth:
Give Him first place in your serv-ice, Con-se-crate ev-'ry part:
He gave Him-self for your ran-som, Gave up His glo-ry a-bove;

Je-sus has set the ex-am-ple, Daunt-less was He, young and brave;
Give, and to you shall be giv-en, God His be-lov-ed Son gave;
Laid down His life with-out mur-mur, You from sin's ru-in to save;

rall.

Give Him your loy-al de-vo-tion, Give Him the best that you have.
Grate-ful-ly seek-ing to serve Him, Give Him the best that you have.
Give Him your heart's ad-o-ra-tion, Give Him the best that you have.

Give of your best to the Mas-ter, Give of the strength of your youth;

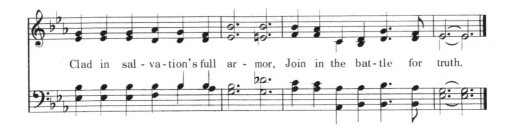

Clad in sal-va-tion's full ar-mor, Join in the bat-tle for truth.

Have Thine Own Way, Lord

124

POLLARD. 5.4.5.4. D.

Adelaide A. Pollard

George C. Stebbins

1. Have Thine own way, Lord! Have Thine own way! Thou art the
2. Have Thine own way, Lord! Have Thine own way! Search me and
3. Have Thine own way, Lord! Have Thine own way! Wound-ed and
4. Have Thine own way, Lord! Have Thine own way! Hold o'er my

pot-ter, I am the clay; Mold me and make me Aft-er Thy
try me, Mas-ter, to-day! Whit-er than snow, Lord, Wash me just
wea-ry, Help me, I pray! Pow-er, all pow-er Sure-ly is
be-ing Ab-so-lute sway! Fill with Thy Spir-it Till all shall

will, While I am wait-ing, Yield-ed and still.
now, As in Thy pres-ence Hum-bly I bow.
Thine! Touch me and heal me, Sav-iour di-vine.
see Christ on-ly, al-ways, Liv-ing in me. A-MEN.

Copyright 1907, Renewal 1935 by G.C. Stebbins. Assigned to Hope Publishing Co. All rights reserved.
Used by permission.

125 Now in the Days of Youth

Walter J. Mathams

DIADEMATA. S.M.D.
George J. Elvey

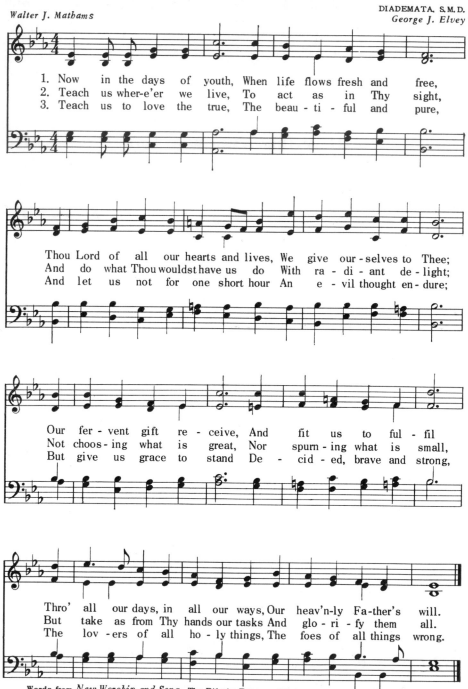

1. Now in the days of youth, When life flows fresh and free,
2. Teach us wher-e'er we live, To act as in Thy sight,
3. Teach us to love the true, The beau-ti-ful and pure,

Thou Lord of all our hearts and lives, We give our-selves to Thee;
And do what Thou wouldst have us do With ra-di-ant de-light;
And let us not for one short hour An e-vil thought en-dure;

Our fer-vent gift re-ceive, And fit us to ful-fil
Not choos-ing what is great, Nor spurn-ing what is small,
But give us grace to stand De-cid-ed, brave and strong,

Thro' all our days, in all our ways, Our heav'n-ly Fa-ther's will.
But take as from Thy hands our tasks And glo-ri-fy them all.
The lov-ers of all ho-ly things, The foes of all things wrong.

Words from *New Worship and Song*. The Pilgrim Press, publisher.

Beneath the Cross of Jesus

ST. CHRISTOPHER. 7.6.8.6.8.6.8.6.

Elizabeth C. Clephane

Frederick C. Maker

1. Be - neath the cross of Je - sus I fain would take my stand,
2. Up - on that cross of Je - sus Mine eye at times can see
3. I take, O Cross, thy shad - ow For my a - bid - ing place;

The shad - ow of a might - y rock With - in a wea - ry land;
The ver - y dy - ing form of One Who suf - fered there for me;
I ask no oth - er sun - shine than The sun - shine of His face;

A home with - in the wil - der - ness, A rest up - on the way,
And from my smit - ten heart with tears Two won - ders I con - fess,
Con - tent to let the world go by, To know no gain or loss,

From the burn - ing of the noon-tide heat And the bur - den of the day.
The won - ders of His glo - rious love And my un - wor - thi - ness.
My sin - ful self my on - ly shame, My glo - ry all the cross.

127 Let Others See Jesus in You

COLEMAN. 8.7.8.8. *with Refrain*

B. B. McKinney

B. B. McKinney

1. While pass-ing thro' this world of sin, And oth-ers your life shall view,
2. Your life's a book be - fore their eyes, They're reading it thro' and thro';
3. Then live for Christ both day and night, Be faith-ful, be brave and true,

Be clean and pure with-out, with-in, Let oth-ers see Je - sus in you.
Say, does it point them to the skies, Do oth-ers see Je - sus in you?
And lead the lost to life and light; Let oth-ers see Je - sus in you.

REFRAIN

Let oth-ers see Je-sus in you, ..Let oth-ers see Je-sus in you; ....

Keep tell-ing the sto-ry, be faith-ful and true, Let oth-ers see Je-sus in you.

© Copyright 1952, Renewal. Broadman Press. All rights reserved. International copyright secured.

Wherever He Leads I'll Go

128

FALLS CREEK. 8.6.8.7. *with Refrain*
B. B. McKinney

B. B. McKinney

1. "Take up thy cross and fol-low Me," I heard my Mas-ter say;
2. He drew me clos-er to His side, I sought His will to know,
3. It may be through the shad-ows dim, Or o'er the storm-y sea,
4. My heart, my life, my all I bring To Christ who loves me so;

"I gave My life to ran-som thee, Sur-ren-der your all to - day."
And in that will I now a-bide, Wher-ev-er He leads I'll go.
I take my cross and fol-low Him, Wher-ev-er He lead-eth me.
He is my Mas-ter, Lord, and King, Wher-ev-er He leads I'll go.

REFRAIN

Wher-ev-er He leads I'll go, . . Wher-ev-er He leads I'll go, ...

I'll fol-low my Christ who loves me so, Wher-ev-er He leads I'll go.

© Copyright 1964. Renewal. Broadman Press. All rights reserved. International copyright secured.

129   O God of Youth, Whose Spirit

Bates G. Burt

LYNNE. 13.10.11.10.
Bates G. Burt

1. O God of youth, whose Spir - it in our hearts is stir - ring
2. Fill Thou our hearts with zeal in ev - ery brave en - deav - or
3. Teach us to know the way of Je - sus Christ, our Mas - ter;
4. May we be true to Him, our Cap - tain of sal - va - tion,

Hope and de - sire for no - ble lives and true,
To right the wrongs that shame this mor - tal life;
Give us His clear - eyed faith, His fear - less heart,
Bear - ing His cross in serv - ice glad and free,

Keep us, we pray Thee, stead - fast and un - err - ing;
Give us the val - iant spir - it that shall nev - er
And through life's dark - ness, dan - ger, and dis - as - ter,
Win - ning the world to that last con - sum - ma - tion

With light and love di - vine our souls en - due.
Fal - ter or fail how - ev - er long the strife.
Oh, may we nev - er from His side de - part.
When all its king-doms shall His king - dom be.   A - MEN.

Words and music used by permission John H. Burt.

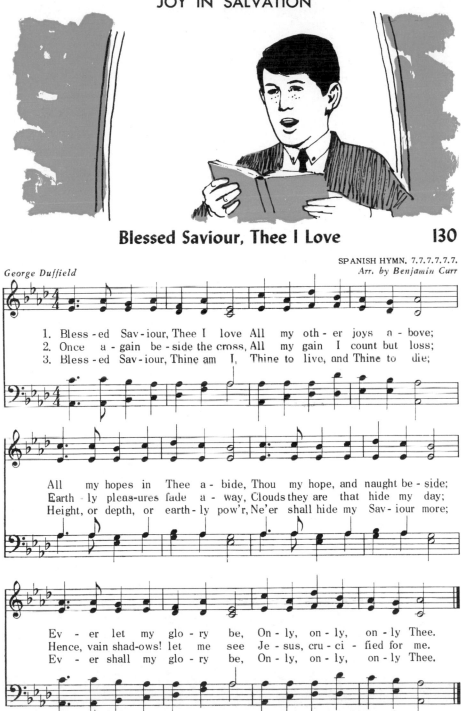

Blessed Saviour, Thee I Love 130

SPANISH HYMN. 7.7.7.7.7.7.
Arr. by Benjamin Carr

George Duffield

1. Bless-ed Sav-iour, Thee I love All my oth-er joys a-bove;
2. Once a-gain be-side the cross, All my gain I count but loss;
3. Bless-ed Sav-iour, Thine am I, Thine to live, and Thine to die;

All my hopes in Thee a-bide, Thou my hope, and naught be-side;
Earth-ly pleas-ures fade a-way, Clouds they are that hide my day;
Height, or depth, or earth-ly pow'r, Ne'er shall hide my Sav-iour more;

Ev-er let my glo-ry be, On-ly, on-ly, on-ly Thee.
Hence, vain shad-ows! let me see Je-sus, cru-ci-fied for me.
Ev-er shall my glo-ry be, On-ly, on-ly, on-ly Thee.

131   Trusting Jesus

Edgar Page Stites

TRUSTING JESUS. 7.7.7.7. *with Refrain*
Ira D. Sankey

1. Sim - ply trust - ing ev - 'ry day, Trust-ing through a storm - y way;
2. Bright - ly doth His Spir - it shine In - to this poor heart of mine;
3. Sing - ing if my way is clear, Pray - ing if the path be drear;
4. Trust - ing Him while life shall last, Trust - ing Him till earth be past;

E - ven when my faith is small, Trust-ing Je - sus, that is all.
While He leads I can - not fall; Trust-ing Je - sus, that is all.
If in dan - ger, for Him call; Trust-ing Je - sus, that is all.
Till with - in the jas - per wall, Trust-ing Je - sus, that is all.

REFRAIN

Trust - ing as the mo - ments fly, Trust - ing as the days go by;

Trust - ing Him what-e'er be - fall, Trust - ing Je - sus, that is all.

'Tis So Sweet to Trust in Jesus

TRUST IN JESUS. 8.7.8.7. *with Refrain*

Louisa M. R. Stead

William J. Kirkpatrick

1. 'Tis so sweet to trust in Je - sus, And to take Him at His word;
2. O how sweet to trust in Je - sus, Just to trust His cleans-ing blood;
3. Yes, 'tis sweet to trust in Je - sus, Just from sin and self to cease;
4. I'm so glad I learned to trust Thee, Precious Je - sus, Sav - iour, friend;

Just to rest up - on His prom-ise, And to know, "Thus saith the Lord."
And in sim - ple faith to plunge me 'Neath the heal - ing, cleans-ing flood!
Just from Je - sus sim - ply tak - ing Life and rest, and joy and peace.
And I know that Thou art with me, Wilt be with me to the end.

REFRAIN

Je - sus, Je - sus, how I trust Him! How I've proved Him o'er and o'er!

Je - sus, Je - sus, pre - cious Je - sus! O for grace to trust Him more!

133 He Lives

Alfred H. Ackley

ACKLEY. *Irregular with Refrain*
Alfred H. Ackley

1. I serve a ris-en Sav-iour, He's in the world to-day; I know that He is liv-ing, what-ev-er men may say; I see His hand of mer-cy, I hear His voice of cheer, And just the time I need Him He's al-ways near.

2. In all the world a-round me I see His lov-ing care, And tho' my heart grows wea-ry I nev-er will de-spair; I know that He is lead-ing thro' all the storm-y blast, The day of His ap-pear-ing will come at last.

3. Re-joice, re-joice, O Christian, lift up your voice and sing E-ter-nal hal-le-lu-jahs to Je-sus Christ the King! The hope of all who seek Him, the help of all who find, None oth-er is so lov-ing, so good and kind.

REFRAIN

He lives, He lives, Christ Je-sus lives to-day! He walks with me and

Copyright 1961. Renewal. The Rodeheaver Company, owner. All rights reserved. Used by permission.

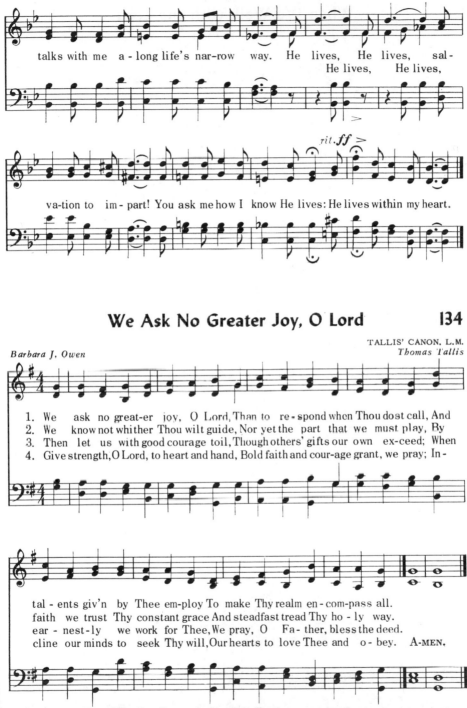

talks with me a-long life's nar-row way. He lives, He lives, sal-
He lives, He lives,

*rit.**ff***

va-tion to im-part! You ask me how I know He lives: He lives within my heart.

We Ask No Greater Joy, O Lord   134

TALLIS' CANON, L.M.
Thomas Tallis

Barbara J. Owen

1. We   ask no great-er joy, O Lord, Than to re-spond when Thou dost call, And
2. We   know not whither Thou wilt guide, Nor yet the part that we must play, By
3. Then let us with good courage toil, Though others' gifts our own ex-ceed; When
4. Give strength, O Lord, to heart and hand, Bold faith and cour-age grant, we pray; In-

tal-ents giv'n by Thee em-ploy To make Thy realm en-com-pass all.
faith we trust Thy constant grace And steadfast tread Thy ho-ly way.
ear-nest-ly we work for Thee, We pray, O Fa-ther, bless the deed.
cline our minds to seek Thy will, Our hearts to love Thee and o-bey. A-MEN.

Words from *Three More New Hymns for Youth by Youth.* Copyright 1957 by the Hymn Society of America. Used by permission.

135 When We Walk with the Lord

John H. Sammis

TRUST AND OBEY. 6.6.9.D. *with Refrain*
Daniel B. Towner

1. When we walk with the Lord In the light of His Word What a glo-ry He
2. Not a bur-den we bear, Not a sor-row we share, But our toil He doth
3. But we nev-er can prove The de-lights of His love Un-til all on the
4. Then in fel-low-ship sweet We will sit at His feet Or we'll walk by His

sheds on our way! While we do His good will, He a-bides with us still,
rich-ly re-pay; Not a grief or a loss, Not a frown or a cross,
al-tar we lay; For the fa-vor He shows And the joy He be-stows
side in the way; What He says we will do, Where He sends we will go;

REFRAIN

And with all who will trust and o-bey.
But is blest if we trust and o-bey.
Are for them who will trust and o-bey.
Nev-er fear, on-ly trust and o-bey.

Trust and o-bey, for there's no oth-er

way To be hap-py in Je-sus, But to trust and o-bey.

Blessed Assurance, Jesus Is Mine

ASSURANCE. 9.10.9.9. *with Refrain*

Fanny J. Crosby

Mrs. Joseph F. Knapp

1. Bless-ed as-sur-ance, Je-sus is mine! Oh, what a fore-taste of
2. Per-fect sub-mis-sion, per-fect de-light, Vi-sions of rap-ture now
3. Per-fect sub-mis-sion, all is at rest, I in my Sav-iour am

glo-ry di-vine! Heir of sal-va-tion, pur-chase of God,
burst on my sight: An-gels de-scend-ing bring from a-bove
hap-py and blest: Watch-ing and wait-ing, look-ing a-bove,

REFRAIN

Born of His Spir-it, wash'd in His blood.
Ech-oes of mer-cy, whis-pers of love. This is my sto-ry, this is my
Fill'd with His goodness, lost in His love.

song, Prais-ing my Sav-iour all the day long; This is my sto-ry,

this is my song, Prais-ing my Sav-iour all the day long.

137 He Keeps Me Singing

Luther B. Bridgers

SWEETEST NAME. 9.7.9.7. *with Refrain*
Luther B. Bridgers

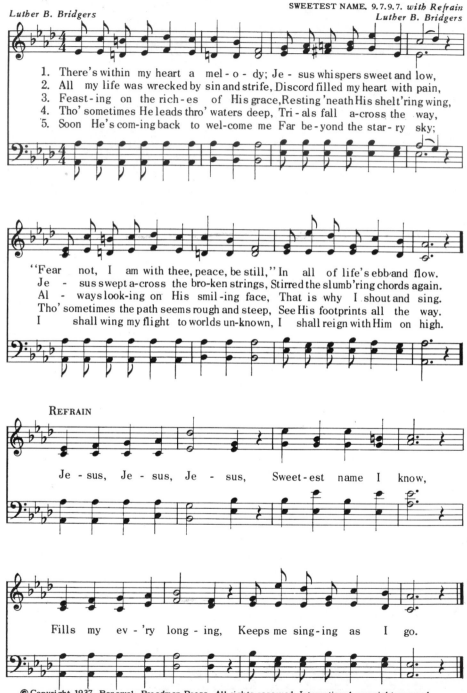

1. There's within my heart a mel-o-dy; Je-sus whispers sweet and low,
2. All my life was wrecked by sin and strife, Discord filled my heart with pain,
3. Feast-ing on the rich-es of His grace, Resting 'neath His shelt'ring wing,
4. Tho' sometimes He leads thro' waters deep, Tri-als fall a-cross the way,
5. Soon He's com-ing back to wel-come me Far be-yond the star-ry sky;

"Fear not, I am with thee, peace, be still," In all of life's ebb and flow.
Je - sus swept a-cross the bro-ken strings, Stirred the slumb'ring chords again.
Al - ways look-ing on His smil-ing face, That is why I shout and sing.
Tho' sometimes the path seems rough and steep, See His footprints all the way.
I shall wing my flight to worlds un-known, I shall reign with Him on high.

REFRAIN

Je - sus, Je - sus, Je - sus, Sweet-est name I know,

Fills my ev-'ry long-ing, Keeps me sing-ing as I go.

© Copyright 1937. Renewal. Broadman Press. All rights reserved. International copyright secured.

Saviour, Teach Me Day by Day 138

POSEN. 7.7.7.7.
Georg C. Strattner

Jane E. Leeson

1. Sav-iour, teach me day by day Love's sweet les-son to o-bey;
2. With a child's glad heart of love At Thy bid-ding may I move,
3. Teach me thus Thy steps to trace, Strong to fol-low in Thy grace,

Sweet-er les-son can-not be, Lov-ing Him who first loved me.
Prompt to serve and fol-low Thee, Lov-ing Him who first loved me.
Learn-ing how to love from Thee, Lov-ing Him who first loved me. A-MEN.

139 Purer in Heart, O God

PURER IN HEART. 6.4.6.4.6.6.4.4.

Fannie Estelle Davison
James H. Fillmore

1. Pur - er in heart, O God, Help me to be;
2. Pur - er in heart, O God, Help me to be;
3. Pur - er in heart, O God, Help me to be,

May I de - vote my life Whol - ly to Thee:
Teach me to do Thy will Most lov - ing - ly:
Un - til Thy ho - ly face One day I see:

Watch Thou my way - ward feet, Guide me with coun - sel sweet;
Be Thou my friend and guide, Let me with Thee a - bide;
Keep me from se - cret sin, Reign Thou my soul with - in;

Pur - er in heart Help me to be.
Pur - er in heart Help me to be.
Pur - er in heart Help me to be.

A - MEN.

In Our Work and in Our Play

ROSSLYN. 7.7.7.7.7.7.
English Melody

Whitfield G. Wills

1. In our work and in our play, Je - sus, ev - er
2. May we in Thy strength sub - due E - vil tem - pers,
3. Chil - dren of the King are we! May we loy - al

with us stay; May we al - ways strive to be
words un - true, Thoughts im - pure, and deeds un - kind
to Him be; Try to please Him ev - 'ry day,

True and faith - ful un - to Thee. Then we truth - ful -
All things hate - ful to Thy mind. Then we truth - ful -
In our work and in our play. Then we truth - ful -

ly can sing, We are chil - dren of the King.
ly can sing, We are chil - dren of the King.
ly can sing, We are chil - dren of the King. A - MEN.

141

Teach Us

PRAYER, L.M.
Robert Graham

Jeana Graham

1. Teach us to fill our own small place
   From day to day with joy and grace:
   That we may find each task to be
   A way for us to wor - ship Thee.

2. Teach us to fol - low in Thy way,
   In ev - 'ry - thing we do or say,
   Let lov - ing kind - ness ev - er be
   A way to show our love for Thee.

3. Teach us, O Lord, our whole life long
   That we choose wise - ly right from wrong,
   So may our lives for - ev - er be
   Ac - cept - a - ble, O Lord, to Thee.

© Copyright 1964, Broadman Press. All rights reserved. International copyright secured.

Growing Like Jesus

Ethel Wendell Trout, alt.

ALL SAINTS, NEW. C.M.D.
Henry S. Cutler

1. O Je - sus, Lad of Naz - a - reth, Help us this day to grow
2. O Je - sus, Lad of Naz - a - reth, Help us this day to grow

In fa - vor with both God and man, As Thou didst, long a - go.
In wis - dom and in stat - ure, too, As Thou didst, long a - go.

Thou wast o - be - dient, hap - py, true, Though with a spir - it free,
Help us to live as Thou didst live, And in our homes to be

There in Thy lov - ing, hum - ble home, O Lad of Gal - i - lee!
O - be - dient, hap - py, kind, and true, O Lad of Gal - i - lee!

Words © Copyright 1927 by Presbyterian Board of Christian Education; renewed 1955; from
Hymns for Junior Worship. Used by permission.

143 More Like Jesus Would I Be

Fanny J. Crosby

MORE LIKE JESUS. 7.7.7.7.D.
William H. Doane

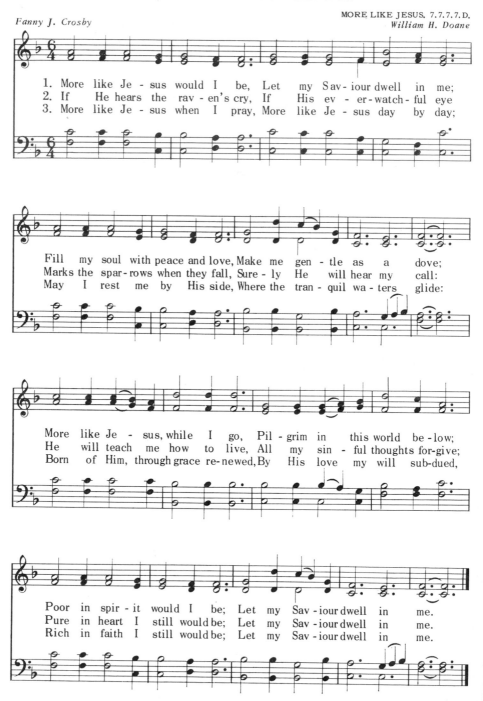

1. More like Je - sus would I be, Let my Sav - iour dwell in me;
2. If He hears the rav - en's cry, If His ev - er - watch - ful eye
3. More like Je - sus when I pray, More like Je - sus day by day;

Fill my soul with peace and love, Make me gen - tle as a dove;
Marks the spar - rows when they fall, Sure - ly He will hear my call:
May I rest me by His side, Where the tran - quil wa - ters glide:

More like Je - sus, while I go, Pil - grim in this world be - low;
He will teach me how to live, All my sin - ful thoughts for - give;
Born of Him, through grace re - newed, By His love my will sub - dued,

Poor in spir - it would I be; Let my Sav - iour dwell in me.
Pure in heart I still would be; Let my Sav - iour dwell in me.
Rich in faith I still would be; Let my Sav - iour dwell in me.

I Would Be True

PEEK. 11. 10. 11. 10.

Howard A. Walter

Joseph Y. Peek

1. I would be true, for there are those who trust me; I would be
2. I would be friend of all—the foe, the friend-less; I would be
3. I would be prayer-ful thro' each bus-y mo-ment; I would be

pure, for there are those who care; I would be strong, for
giv-ing, and for-get the gift; I would be hum-ble,
con-stant-ly in touch with God; I would be tuned to

there is much to suf-fer; I would be brave, for there is
for I know my weak-ness; I would look up, and laugh, and
hear the slight-est whis-per; I would have faith to keep the

much to dare, I would be brave, for there is much to dare.
love, and lift, I would look up, and laugh, and love, and lift.
path Christ trod, I would have faith to keep the path Christ trod.

Saviour, in the Words I Say

Josephine L. Baldwin

MARIETTA. 7.7.7.7.
James D. Cram

1. Sav - iour, in the words I say May I fol - low
2. Show me how to play each game Fair and square, as
3. In my home, at play, at school, May I keep the

Thine own way; And in all the deeds I do
in Thy Name; Lose the con - test if I must,
Gold - en Rule; Brave - ly face the hard - est test,

Show a spir - it fair and true.
But in ev - 'ry act be just.
Love my neigh - bors, do my best.

Words from *Services and Songs for Use in the Junior Department.* Abingdon Press. Used by permission. Music © Copyright 1964, Broadman Press. All rights reserved. International copyright secured.

O Master of the Loving Heart

Calvin W. Laufer

SERENITY. C.M.
William V. Wallace

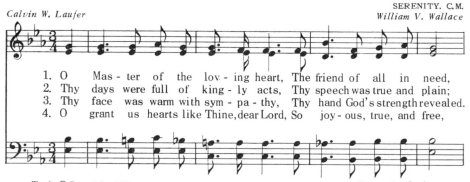

1. O Mas - ter of the lov - ing heart, The friend of all in need,
2. Thy days were full of king - ly acts, Thy speech was true and plain;
3. Thy face was warm with sym - pa - thy, Thy hand God's strength revealed.
4. O grant us hearts like Thine, dear Lord, So joy - ous, true, and free,

Words © Copyright 1927 by C. W. Laufer; renewed 1955 by E. B. Laufer; from *Hymns for Junior Worship.* Used by permission.

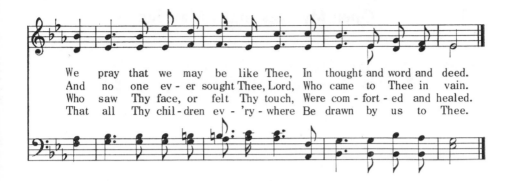

We pray that we may be like Thee, In thought and word and deed.
And no one ev - er sought Thee, Lord, Who came to Thee in vain.
Who saw Thy face, or felt Thy touch, Were com - fort - ed and healed.
That all Thy chil - dren ev - 'ry - where Be drawn by us to Thee.

Oh, that the Lord Would Guide My Ways 147

EVAN. C.M.
Isaac Watts
William H. Havergal

1. Oh, that the Lord would guide my ways To
2. Or - der my foot - steps by Thy Word, And
3. Make me to walk in Thy com - mands——'Tis

keep His stat - utes still! Oh, that my God would
make my heart sin - cere; Let sin have no do -
a de - light - ful road— Nor let my head or

grant me grace To know and do His will!
min - ion, Lord, But keep my con - science clear.
heart or hands Of - fend a - gainst my God.

Open My Eyes that I May See

SCOTT. *Irregular*
Clara H. Scott

Clara H. Scott

1. O-pen my eyes that I may see Glimps-es of truth Thou hast for me;
2. O-pen my ears that I may hear Voic - es of truth Thou sendest clear;
3. O-pen my mouth and let me bear Glad - ly the warm truth ev -'ry-where;

Place in my hands the won-der-ful key That shall un-clasp, and set me free:
And while the wave-notes fall on my ear, Ev - 'ry-thing false will dis - ap-pear:
O - pen my heart, and let me pre-pare Love with Thy chil-dren thus to share:

Si -lent-ly now I wait for Thee, Read-y, my God, Thy will to see;
Si -lent-ly now I wait for Thee, Read-y, my God, Thy will to see;
Si -lent-ly now I wait for Thee, Read-y, my God, Thy will to see;

O - pen my eyes, il - lu -mine me, Spir - it di - vine!
O - pen my ears, il - lu -mine me, Spir - it di - vine!
O - pen my heart, il - lu -mine me, Spir - it di - vine! A-MEN.

Teach Me, O Lord, I Pray

DIADEMATA. S.M.D.

G. Kearnie Keegan

George J. Elvey

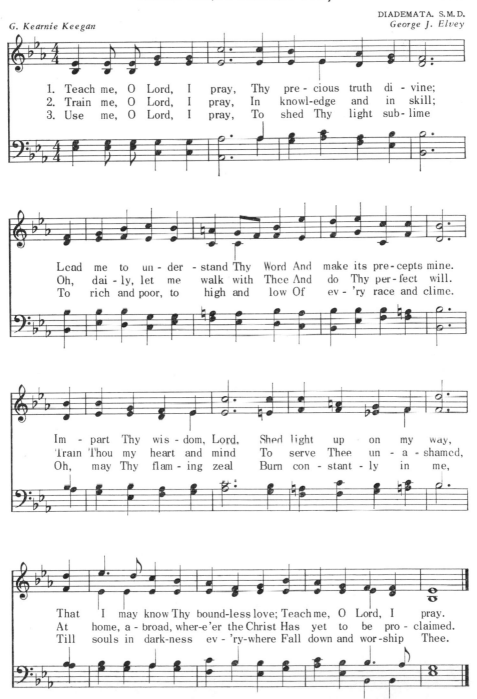

1. Teach me, O Lord, I pray, Thy pre - cious truth di - vine;
2. Train me, O Lord, I pray, In knowl-edge and in skill;
3. Use me, O Lord, I pray, To shed Thy light sub - lime

Lead me to un - der - stand Thy Word And make its pre - cepts mine.
Oh, dai - ly, let me walk with Thee And do Thy per - fect will.
To rich and poor, to high and low Of ev - 'ry race and clime.

Im - part Thy wis - dom, Lord, Shed light up - on my way,
Train Thou my heart and mind To serve Thee un - a - shamed,
Oh, may Thy flam - ing zeal Burn con - stant - ly in me,

That I may know Thy bound-less love; Teach me, O Lord, I pray.
At home, a - broad, wher-e'er the Christ Has yet to be pro - claimed.
Till souls in dark-ness ev - 'ry-where Fall down and wor-ship Thee.

© Copyright 1959, Broadman Press. All rights reserved. International copyright secured.

150 More About Jesus

Eliza E. Hewitt

SWENEY. L.M. *with Refrain*
John R. Sweney

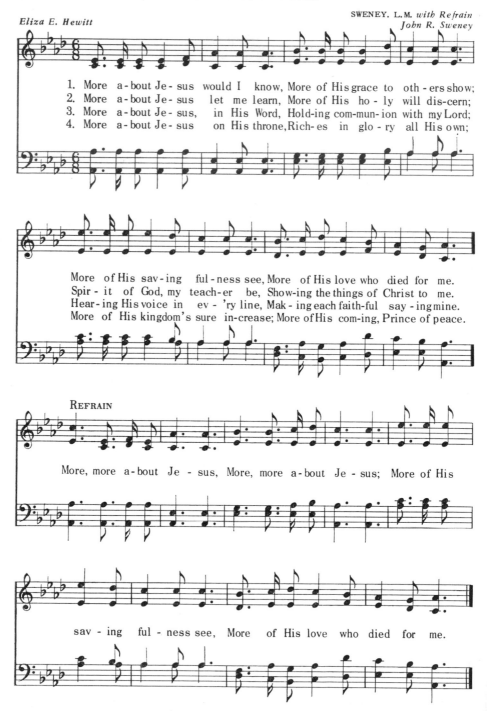

1. More a-bout Je-sus would I know, More of His grace to oth-ers show;
2. More a-bout Je-sus let me learn, More of His ho-ly will dis-cern;
3. More a-bout Je-sus, in His Word, Hold-ing com-mun-ion with my Lord;
4. More a-bout Je-sus on His throne, Rich-es in glo-ry all His own;

More of His sav-ing ful-ness see, More of His love who died for me.
Spir-it of God, my teach-er be, Show-ing the things of Christ to me.
Hear-ing His voice in ev-'ry line, Mak-ing each faith-ful say-ing mine.
More of His kingdom's sure in-crease; More of His com-ing, Prince of peace.

REFRAIN

More, more a-bout Je-sus, More, more a-bout Je-sus; More of His

sav-ing ful-ness see, More of His love who died for me.

PRAYER

Teach Us, Dear Lord, to Pray 151

GREENE. S.M.

Calvin W. Laufer

Edward Shippen Barnes

1. Teach us, dear Lord, to pray, To trust Thee as we should;
2. Thy love sur-rounds us all With con - stant, pa - tient care;

And help us feel that, come what may, Thy gifts are al - ways good.
Thy ten - der heart, be - fore we call, A - waits our ear - nest prayer. A-MEN.

Words © Copyright 1927 by C. W. Laufer; renewed 1955 by E. B. Laufer. Used by permission. Music © Copyright 1927 by Presbyterian Board of Christian Education; renewed 1955. From *Hymns for Junior Worship.* Used by permission.

152 Sweet Hour of Prayer

William W. Walford

SWEET HOUR. L.M.D.
William B. Bradbury

1. Sweet hour of prayer, sweet hour of prayer, That calls me from a world of care,
2. Sweet hour of prayer, sweet hour of prayer, The joys I feel, the bliss I share
3. Sweet hour of prayer, sweet hour of prayer, Thy wings shall my pe - ti - tion bear

And bids me at my Fa - ther's throne, Make all my wants and wish - es known!
Of those whose anx-ious spir - its burn With strong de-sires for thy re - turn!
To Him, whose truth and faith-ful - ness En - gage the wait - ing soul to bless:

In sea - sons of dis - tress and grief, My soul has of - ten found re - lief,
With such I has - ten to the place Where God my Sav - iour shows His face,
And since He bids me seek His face, Be - lieve His word, and trust His grace,

And oft es-caped the temp-ter's snare By thy re - turn, sweet hour of prayer.
And glad - ly take my sta - tion there, And wait for thee, sweet hour of prayer.
I'll cast on Him my ev - 'ry care, And wait for thee, sweet hour of prayer.

Speak to My Heart

HOLCOMB. 7.6.7.6. *with Refrain*

B. B. McKinney

B. B. McKinney

1. Speak to my heart, Lord Je - sus, Speak that my soul may hear;
2. Speak to my heart, Lord Je - sus, Purge me from ev - 'ry sin;
3. Speak to my heart, Lord Je - sus, It is no long - er mine:

Speak to my heart, Lord Je - sus, Calm ev - 'ry doubt and fear.
Speak to my heart, Lord Je - sus, Help me the lost to win.
Speak to my heart, Lord Je - sus, I would be whol - ly Thine.

REFRAIN

Speak to my heart, oh, speak to my heart, Speak to my heart, I pray;

Yield - ed and still, seek - ing Thy will, Oh, speak to my heart to - day.

© Copyright 1955. Renewal. Broadman Press. All rights reserved. International copyright secured.

154   Father, We Thank Thee

WE THANK THEE. L.M.

Rebecca J. Weston

Daniel Batchellor

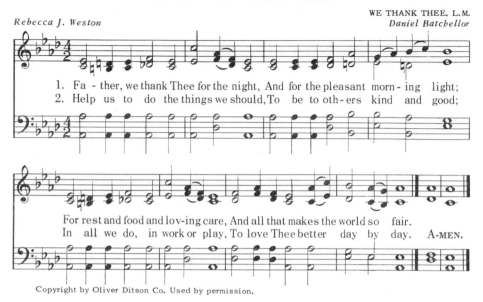

1. Fa - ther, we thank Thee for the night, And for the pleasant morn - ing light;
2. Help us to do the things we should, To be to oth - ers kind and good;

For rest and food and lov-ing care, And all that makes the world so fair.
In all we do, in work or play, To love Thee better day by day. A-MEN.

Copyright by Oliver Ditson Co. Used by permission.

155   My Singing Is a Prayer

VERMONT. C.M.

Novella D. Preston

David H. Williams

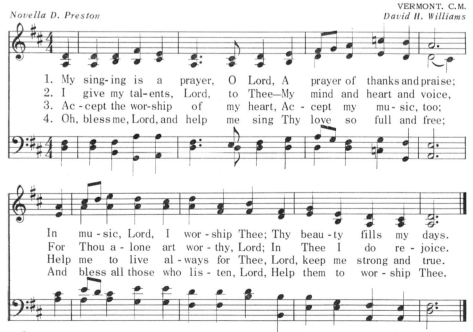

1. My sing-ing is a prayer, O Lord, A prayer of thanks and praise;
2. I give my tal - ents, Lord, to Thee—My mind and heart and voice,
3. Ac - cept the wor-ship of my heart, Ac - cept my mu - sic, too;
4. Oh, bless me, Lord, and help me sing Thy love so full and free;

In mu - sic, Lord, I wor-ship Thee; Thy beau - ty fills my days.
For Thou a - lone art wor - thy, Lord; In Thee I do re - joice.
Help me to live al - ways for Thee, Lord, keep me strong and true.
And bless all those who lis - ten, Lord, Help them to wor - ship Thee.

© Copyright 1964, Broadman Press. All rights reserved. International copyright secured.

Saviour, Like a Shepherd Lead Us 156

From "Hymns for the Young," 1836
Ascr. to Dorothy A. Thrupp

BRADBURY. 8.7.8.7.D.
William B. Bradbury

1. Sav - iour, like a shep - herd lead us, Much we need Thy ten -der care;
2. We are Thine; do Thou be - friend us, Be the guard-ian of our way;
3. Thou hast prom-ised to re - ceive us, Poor and sin -ful though we be;
4. Ear - ly let us seek Thy fa - vor; Ear - ly let us do Thy will;

In Thy pleas-ant pas-tures feed us, For our use Thy folds pre-pare:
Keep Thy flock from sin, de - fend us, Seek us when we go a- stray:
Thou hast mer - cy to re - lieve us, Grace to cleanse, and pow'r to free:
Bless-ed Lord and on - ly Sav - iour, With Thy love our bos-oms fill:

Bless-ed Je-sus, bless-ed Je - sus, Thou hast bought us, Thine we are;
Bless-ed Je-sus, bless-ed Je - sus, Hear, O hear us when we pray;
Bless-ed Je-sus, bless-ed Je - sus, Ear - ly let us turn to Thee;
Bless-ed Je-sus, bless-ed Je - sus, Thou hast loved us, love us still;

Bless-ed Je-sus, bless-ed Je - sus, Thou hast bought us, Thine we are.
Bless-ed Je-sus, bless-ed Je - sus, Hear, O hear us when we pray.
Bless-ed Je-sus, bless-ed Je - sus, Ear - ly let us turn to Thee.
Bless-ed Je-sus, bless-ed Je - sus, Thou hast loved us, love us still.

157　Father Almighty, Bless Us with Thy Blessing

"Berwick Hymnal," 1886

SIBLEY. 11.11.11.10.
Talmage W. Dean

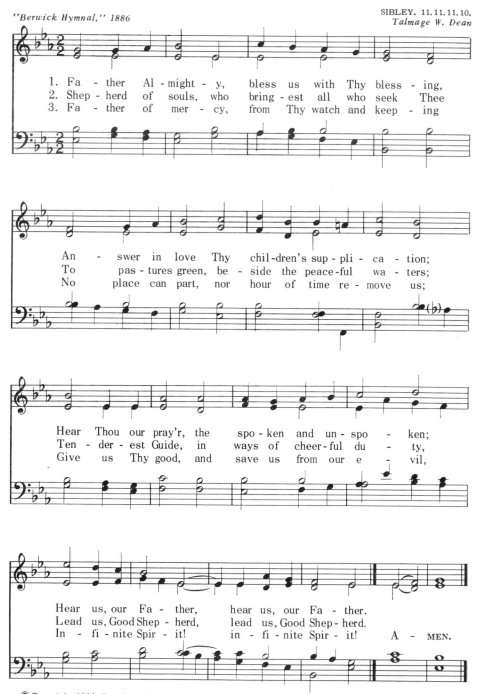

1. Fa - ther Al - might - y, bless us with Thy bless - ing,
2. Shep - herd of souls, who bring - est all who seek Thee
3. Fa - ther of mer - cy, from Thy watch and keep - ing

An - swer in love Thy chil-dren's sup - pli - ca - tion;
To pas - tures green, be - side the peace-ful wa - ters;
No place can part, nor hour of time re - move us;

Hear Thou our pray'r, the spo - ken and un - spo - ken;
Ten - der - est Guide, in ways of cheer - ful du - ty,
Give us Thy good, and save us from our e - vil,

Hear us, our Fa - ther, hear us, our Fa - ther.
Lead us, Good Shep - herd, lead us, Good Shep - herd.
In - fi - nite Spir - it! in - fi - nite Spir - it! A - MEN.

© Copyright 1964, Broadman Press. All rights reserved. International copyright secured.

Our Father in Heaven

158

ST. MICHEL'S. 11.11.11.11.

Sarah J. Hale

From William Gawler's "Hymns and Psalms," 1789

1. Our Father in heaven, we hallow Thy name:
2. Forgive our transgressions, and teach us to know

May Thy kingdom holy on earth be the same:
That humble compassion which pardons each foe;

O give to us daily our portion of bread:
Keep us from temptation, from evil and sin,

It is from Thy bounty that all must be fed.
And Thine be the glory, forever! Amen! A-MEN.

159 **Thanks for Homes**

John Haynes Holmes

TALLIS' CANON. L.M.
Thomas Tallis

1. O Fa - ther, Thou who giv-est all The boun-ty of Thy per-fect love, We
2. We thank Thee for the grace of home, For moth-er's love and fa-ther's care; For
3. For eyes to see and ears to hear, For hands to serve and arms to lift, For
4. For faith to con-quer doubt and fear, For love to an - swer ev - 'ry call, For

thank Thee that up - on us fall Such ten- der blessings from a - bove.
friends and teach-ers—all who come Our joys and hopes and fears to share.
shoul- ders broad and strong to bear, For feet to run on er - rands swift.
strength to do, and will to dare, We thank Thee, O Thou Lord of all. A-MEN.

Words used by permission John Haynes Holmes.

Happy the Home When God Is There 160

ST. AGNES, C.M.
John B. Dykes

Henry Ware, the younger

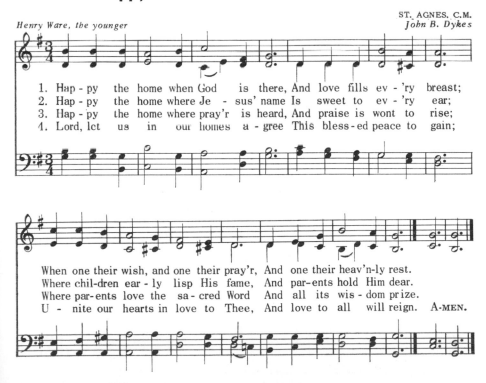

1. Hap-py the home when God is there, And love fills ev-'ry breast;
2. Hap-py the home where Je - sus' name Is sweet to ev-'ry ear;
3. Hap-py the home where pray'r is heard, And praise is wont to rise;
4. Lord, let us in our homes a - gree This bless-ed peace to gain;

When one their wish, and one their pray'r, And one their heav'n-ly rest.
Where chil-dren ear - ly lisp His fame, And par-ents hold Him dear.
Where par-ents love the sa - cred Word And all its wis - dom prize.
U - nite our hearts in love to Thee, And love to all will reign. A-MEN.

God, Give Us Christian Homes!

B. B. McKinney

CHRISTIAN HOME. Irregular
B. B. McKinney

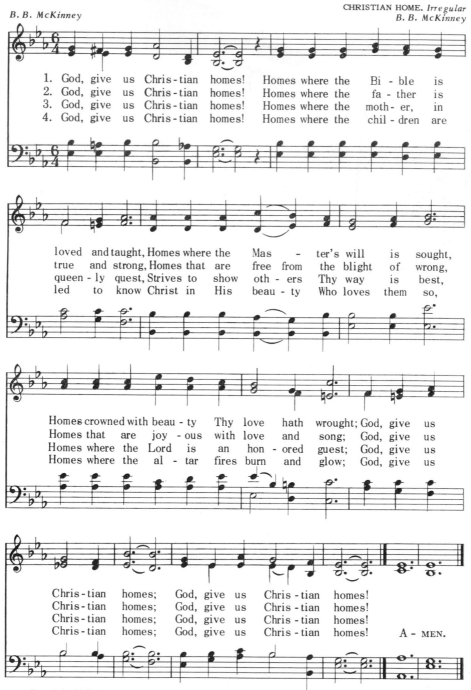

1. God, give us Chris-tian homes! Homes where the Bi - ble is loved and taught, Homes where the Mas - ter's will is sought, Homes crowned with beau - ty Thy love hath wrought; God, give us Chris-tian homes; God, give us Chris - tian homes!
2. God, give us Chris-tian homes! Homes where the fa - ther is true and strong, Homes that are free from the blight of wrong, Homes that are joy - ous with love and song; God, give us Chris-tian homes; God, give us Chris - tian homes!
3. God, give us Chris-tian homes! Homes where the moth- er, in queen - ly quest, Strives to show oth - ers Thy way is best, Homes where the Lord is an hon - ored guest; God, give us Chris-tian homes; God, give us Chris - tian homes!
4. God, give us Chris-tian homes! Homes where the chil - dren are led to know Christ in His beau - ty Who loves them so, Homes where the al - tar fires burn and glow; God, give us Chris-tian homes; God, give us Chris - tian homes! A - MEN.

Copyright 1949, Broadman Press. All rights reserved.

THE CHURCH

I Love Thy Kingdom, Lord

162

ST. THOMAS. S.M.
Aaron Williams

Timothy Dwight

1. I love Thy king-dom, Lord, The house of Thine a-bode,
2. I love Thy church, O God! Her walls be-fore Thee stand,
3. Be-yond my high-est joy I prize her heav'n-ly ways,
4. Sure as Thy truth shall last, To Zi-on shall be giv'n

The church our blest Re-deem-er saved With His own pre-cious blood.
Dear as the ap-ple of Thine eye, And grav-en on Thy hand.
Her sweet com-mun-ion, sol-emn vows, Her hymns of love and praise.
The bright-est glo-ries earth can yield, And bright-er bliss of heav'n.

163 Houses of Worship

WORSHIP. 8.4.8.4.D.
Charles F. Gounod
Arr. by J. W. Cole

Edith Lovell Thomas

1. Glad-ly to the house of wor-ship Come we to-day,
2. Some de-light in coun-try chap-el Built on a hill;

Thanks to give for qui-et church-es Where peo-ple pray;
Oth-ers kneel in great ca-the-dral Dim-lit and still;

For the or-gan mu-sic sound-ing Far off and near;
Tem-ple con-gre-ga-tions sing the Psalms loved of yore;

For the high sun-light-ed win-dows, Col-ored or clear.
All are set a-part for wor-ship, God to a-dore.

Words by Edith Lovell Thomas. From *The Whole World Singing* by Edith Lovell Thomas.
©Copyright 1950, Friendship Press. Used by permission.

His Own Church

AUSTRIAN HYMN. 8.7.8.7.D.

Wilhelmina D'A. Stephens

Franz J. Haydn

1. Long a-go the friends of Je-sus Who had lived with Him each day
2. We would al-so strive to please Him, In His fel-low-ship would live;

Met to-geth-er for His wor-ship; Oth-ers fol-lowed in their way:
So we band our-selves to-geth-er, All our lives to Him to give:

Bound to-geth-er in one bod-y, Je-sus' friends the whole world o'er-
Tell-ing oth-ers of His good-ness, Win-ning them to love Him, too—

His own Church, on His word founded, Him to hon-or ev-er-more.
His own Church, through all the a-ges, In the world His work to do.

Words © Copyright 1940 by Presbyterian Board of Christian Education; from *Hymns for Junior Worship.* Used by permission.

165 The Church's One Foundation

Samuel J. Stone

AURELIA. 7.6.7.6.D.
Samuel S. Wesley

1. The church-'s one foun-da - tion Is Je - sus Christ her Lord;
2. E - lect from ev - 'ry na - tion, Yet one o'er all the earth,
3. 'Mid toil and trib - u - la - tion, And tu - mult of her war,
4. Yet she on earth hath un - ion With God the Three in One,

She is His new cre - a - tion, By Spir - it and the Word:
Her char - ter of sal - va - tion, One Lord, one faith, one birth;
She waits the con - sum - ma - tion Of peace for - ev - er - more;
And mys - tic sweet com-mun - ion With those whose rest is won;

From heav'n He came and sought her To be His ho - ly bride,
One ho - ly name she bless - es, Par - takes one ho - ly food,
Till with the vi - sion glo - rious, Her long - ing eyes are blest,
O hap - py ones and ho - ly! Lord, give us grace that we,

With His own blood He bought her, And for her life He died.
And to one hope she press - es, With ev - 'ry grace en - dued.
And the great church vic - to - rious Shall be the church at rest.
Like them, the meek and low - ly, On high may dwell with Thee.

O Jesus, I Have Promised

John E. Bode

ANGEL'S STORY. 7.6.7.6.D.
Arthur H. Mann

1. O Je - sus, I have prom - ised To serve Thee to the end;
2. O Je - sus, Thou hast prom - ised To all who fol - low Thee,
3. O let me feel Thee near me! The world is ev - er near;
4. O let me hear Thee speak - ing In ac - cents clear and still,

Be Thou for - ev - er near me, My Mas - ter and my friend;
That where Thou art in glo - ry There shall Thy serv - ant be;
I see the sights that daz - zle, The tempt - ing sounds I hear;
A - bove the storms of pas - sion, The mur - murs of self - will.

I shall not fear the bat - tle If Thou art by my side,
And, Je - sus, I have prom - ised To serve Thee to the end;
My foes are ev - er near me, A - round me and with - in;
O speak to re - as - sure me, To has - ten or con - trol!

Nor wan - der from the path - way If Thou wilt be my guide.
O give me grace to fol - low My Mas - ter and my friend!
But, Je - sus, draw Thou near - er And shield my soul from sin.
O speak, and make me lis - ten, Thou guard - ian of my soul! A - MEN.

167   Our Church Proclaims God's Love and Care

BOYTER. L.M.

Mabel Niedermeyer McCaw

Annette Wheeler

1. Our church pro-claims God's love and care To all who work and wor-ship there, Who sing to-geth-er hymns of praise, And pray'rs of glad thanks-giv-ing raise.
2. Her hands reach out in serv-ice through Kind, help-ful deeds that we must do For show-ing folks in ev-'ry land The world of love that He has planned.
3. Glad-ly we come our praise to sing, And gifts of friend-ly serv-ice bring; We, too, would know God's love and care, And work and joy with oth-ers share.

Words © Copyright 1940 by Presbyterian Board of Christian Education; from *Hymns for Junior Worship.* Used by permission.
Music © Copyright 1957, Broadman Press. All rights reserved. International copyright secured.

168   In Memory of the Saviour's Love

ST. PETER. C.M.

Thomas Cotterill

Alexander R. Reinagle

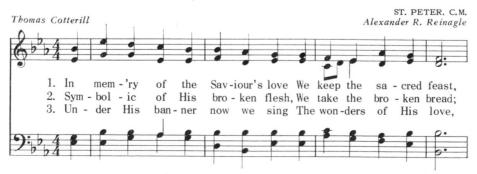

1. In mem-'ry of the Sav-iour's love We keep the sa-cred feast,
2. Sym-bol-ic of His bro-ken flesh, We take the bro-ken bread;
3. Un-der His ban-ner now we sing The won-ders of His love,

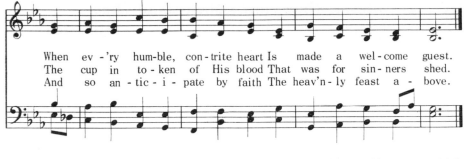

When ev-'ry hum-ble, con-trite heart Is made a wel-come guest.
The cup in to-ken of His blood That was for sin-ners shed.
And so an-tic-i-pate by faith The heav'n-ly feast a-bove.

Thy Supper, Lord, Before Us Spread 169

REYNOLDS. L.M.

Joseph F. Green, Jr.

Irving Wolfe

1. Thy sup-per, Lord, be-fore us spread, The cup be-
2. Thy sac-ri-fice was for our gain; To save us
3. In fel-low-ship with Thee we feel That Thou art
4. Now may the wor-ship we know here Re-mind us

side the bro-ken bread, Re-minds us of Thy life laid
Thou didst bear the pain. Thy love is clear for all to
here, Thy pres-ence real; For Thou hast ris-en and dost
al-ways Thou art near; Help us to live our lives each

down— The shame-ful cross, the thorn-y crown.
see; We bow in thank-ful prayer to Thee.
live With-in our hearts,— new life to give.
day In love and faith, O Lord, we pray.

© Copyright 1961, 1964, Broadman Press. All rights reserved. International copyright secured.

170   Jesus, Thou Hast Called Us to Thee

Joseph F. Green, Jr.

LOVE DIVINE. 8.7.8.7.D.

John Zundel

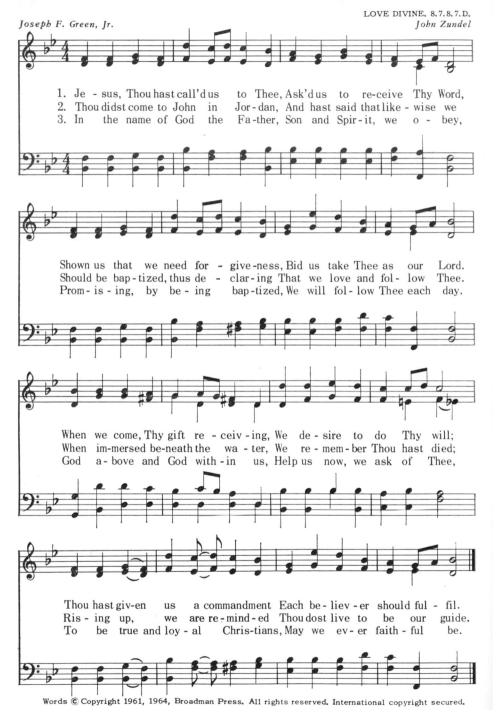

1. Je - sus, Thou hast call'd us   to Thee, Ask'd us to re-ceive Thy Word,
2. Thou didst come to John in   Jor-dan, And hast said that like - wise we
3. In   the name of God the   Fa-ther, Son and Spir-it, we   o - bey,

Shown us that we need for - give-ness, Bid us take Thee as   our   Lord.
Should be bap-tized, thus de - clar-ing That we love and fol - low   Thee.
Prom-is-ing, by be - ing   bap-tized, We will fol-low Thee each   day.

When we come, Thy gift re - ceiv-ing, We de-sire to do   Thy   will;
When im-mersed be-neath the   wa - ter, We re-mem-ber Thou hast died;
God   a-bove and God with-in   us, Help us now, we ask of   Thee,

Thou hast giv-en   us   a commandment Each be-liev-er should ful - fil.
Ris - ing up,   we   are re-mind-ed Thou dost live to   be   our   guide.
To   be true and loy - al   Chris-tians, May we ev-er faith - ful   be.

Words © Copyright 1961, 1964, Broadman Press. All rights reserved. International copyright secured.

Forward Through the Ages

ST. GERTRUDE. 6.5.6.5.D. *with Refrain*

Frederick L. Hosmer

Arthur S. Sullivan

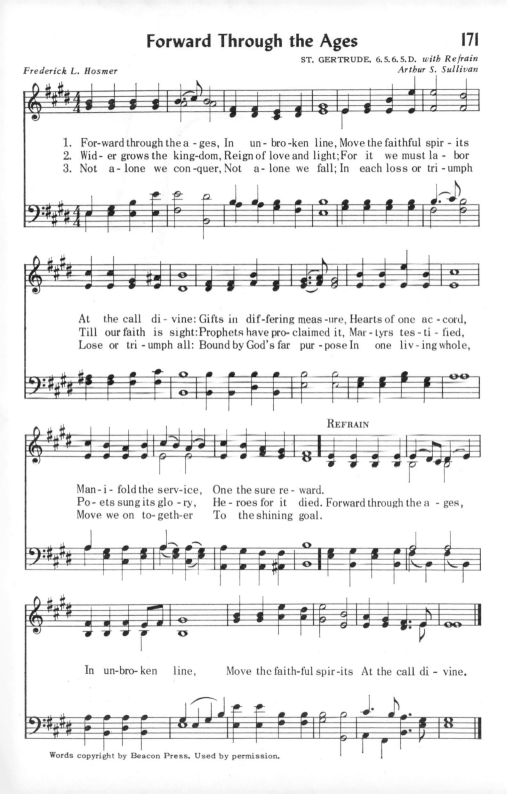

1. For-ward through the a - ges, In un - bro-ken line, Move the faithful spir - its
2. Wid- er grows the king-dom, Reign of love and light; For it we must la - bor
3. Not a - lone we con-quer, Not a - lone we fall; In each loss or tri - umph

At the call di - vine: Gifts in dif-fering meas-ure, Hearts of one ac-cord,
Till our faith is sight: Prophets have pro- claimed it, Mar - tyrs tes - ti - fied,
Lose or tri - umph all: Bound by God's far pur -pose In one liv-ing whole,

REFRAIN

Man-i- fold the serv-ice, One the sure re - ward.
Po- ets sung its glo - ry, He - roes for it died. Forward through the a - ges,
Move we on to-geth-er To the shining goal.

In un-bro-ken line, Move the faith-ful spir-its At the call di - vine.

Words copyright by Beacon Press. Used by permission.

CHRISTIAN SOLDIERS

172   Fight the Good Fight

PENTECOST. L.M.
William Boyd

John S. B. Monsell

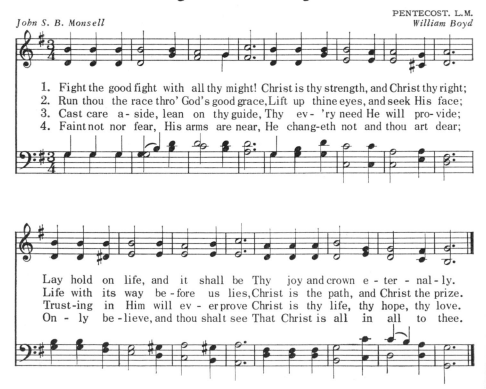

1. Fight the good fight with all thy might! Christ is thy strength, and Christ thy right;
2. Run thou the race thro' God's good grace, Lift up thine eyes, and seek His face;
3. Cast care a-side, lean on thy guide, Thy ev-'ry need He will pro-vide;
4. Faint not nor fear, His arms are near, He chang-eth not and thou art dear;

Lay hold on life, and it shall be Thy joy and crown e-ter-nal-ly.
Life with its way be-fore us lies, Christ is the path, and Christ the prize.
Trust-ing in Him will ev-er prove Christ is thy life, thy hope, thy love.
On-ly be-lieve, and thou shalt see That Christ is all in all to thee.

Onward, Christian Soldiers

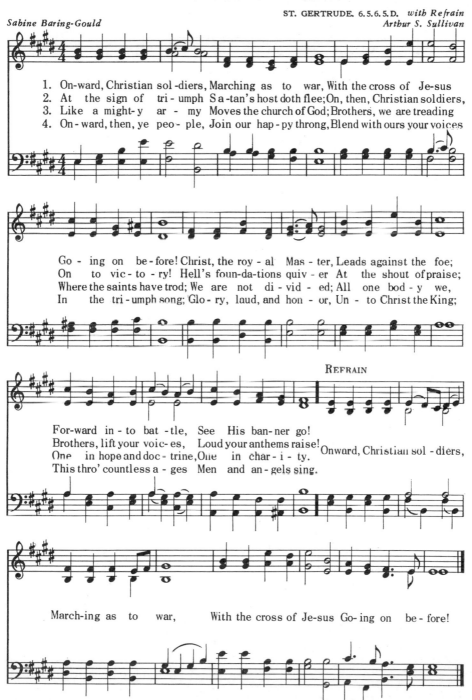

ST. GERTRUDE. 6.5.6.5.D. *with Refrain*

Sabine Baring-Gould

Arthur S. Sullivan

173

1. On-ward, Christian sol-diers, Marching as to war, With the cross of Je-sus
2. At the sign of tri-umph Sa-tan's host doth flee; On, then, Christian soldiers,
3. Like a might-y ar-my Moves the church of God; Brothers, we are treading
4. On-ward, then, ye peo-ple, Join our hap-py throng, Blend with ours your voices

Go-ing on be-fore! Christ, the roy-al Mas-ter, Leads against the foe;
On to vic-to-ry! Hell's foun-da-tions quiv-er At the shout of praise;
Where the saints have trod; We are not di-vid-ed; All one bod-y we,
In the tri-umph song; Glo-ry, laud, and hon-or, Un-to Christ the King;

REFRAIN

For-ward in-to bat-tle, See His ban-ner go!
Brothers, lift your voic-es, Loud your anthems raise!
One in hope and doc-trine, One in char-i-ty.
This thro' countless a-ges Men and an-gels sing.

Onward, Christian sol-diers,

March-ing as to war, With the cross of Je-sus Go-ing on be-fore!

174   March On, O Soul, with Strength

George T. Coster

ARTHUR'S SEAT. 6.6.6.6.8.8.
Arr. from John Goss

1. March on, O soul, with strength! Like those strong men of old,
2. The sons of fa - thers we, By whom our faith is taught
3. March on, O soul, with strength, As strong the bat - tle rolls!
4. Not long the con - flict: soon The ho - ly war shall cease,

Who, 'gainst en - thron - ed wrong, Stood con - fi -
To fear no ill, to fight The ho - ly
'Gainst lies and lusts and wrongs, Let cour - age
Faith's war - fare end - ed, won The home of

dent and bold; Who, thrust in pris'n or cast to flame,
fight they fought: He - ro - ic war - riors, ne'er from Christ,
rule our souls: In keen - est strife, Lord, may we stand,
end - less peace! Look up! the vic - tor's crown at length!

Still made their glo - - ry in Thy name.
By an - y lure or guile, en - ticed.
Up - held and strength - ened by Thy hand.
March on, O soul, march on, with strength! A - MEN.

Dare to Be Brave, Dare to Be True

COURAGE. *Irregular with Refrain*

W. J. Rooper

Duncan Hume

1. Dare to be brave, dare to be true, Strive for the right, for the
2. Dare to be brave, dare to be true, God is your Fa - ther, He
3. Dare to be brave, dare to be true, God grant you cour - age to

Lord is with you; Fight with sin brave - ly, fight and be strong,
watch - es o'er you; He knows your tri - als; when your heart quails,
car - ry you through; Try to help oth - ers, ev - er be kind,

REFRAIN

Christ is your cap - tain, fear on - ly what's wrong.
Call Him to res - cue, His grace nev - er fails. Fight then, good sol - diers,
Let the op - pressed a strong friend in you find.

fight and be brave, Christ is your cap - tain, might - y to save.

Faith of Our Fathers

ST. CATHERINE. 8.8.8.8.8.8.
Henri F. Hemy
Ad. by James G. Walton

Frederick W. Faber

1. Faith of our fa - thers! liv - ing still In spite of dun - geon,
2. Faith of our fa - thers! we will strive To win all na - tions
3. Faith of our fa - thers! we will love Both friend and foe in

fire, and sword, O how our hearts beat high with joy
un - to thee, And through the truth that comes from God
all our strife, And preach thee, too, as love knows how

When-e'er we hear that glo - rious word! Faith of our fa - thers,
Man - kind shall then be tru - ly free: Faith of our fa - thers,
By kind - ly words and vir - tuous life: Faith of our fa - thers,

ho - ly faith! We will be true to thee till death.
ho - ly faith! We will be true to thee till death.
ho - ly faith! We will be true to thee till death. A-MEN.

Who Is on the Lord's Side?

Frances R. Havergal

ARMAGEDDON. 6.5.6.5.6.5.D.
Arr. by John Goss

1. Who is on the Lord's side? Who will serve the King? Who will be His help-ers
2. Fierce may be the con-flict, Strong may be the foe, But the King's own ar-my
3. Cho-sen to be sol-diers In an al-ien land, Cho-sen, called and faith-ful,

Oth-er lives to bring? Who will leave the world's side? Who will face the foe?
None can o-ver-throw; Round His stand-ard rang-ing, Vic-t'ry is se-cure,
For our captain's band; In the serv-ice roy-al Let us not grow cold,

Who is on the Lord's side? Who for Him will go? By Thy call of mer-cy,
For His truth un-chang-ing Makes the tri-umph sure: Joy-ful-ly en-list-ing
Let us be right loy-al, No-ble, true, and bold: Mas-ter, Thou wilt keep us,

By Thy grace di-vine, We are on the Lord's side, Sav-iour, we are Thine.
By Thy grace di-vine, We are on the Lord's side, Sav-iour, we are Thine.
By Thy grace di-vine, Al-ways on the Lord's side, Sav-iour, we are Thine.

178 The Son of God Goes Forth to War

Reginald Heber

ALL SAINTS, NEW. C.M.D.
Henry S. Cutler

1. The Son of God goes forth to war, A king-ly crown to gain;
2. The mar-tyr first, whose ea-gle eye Could pierce be-yond the grave,
3. A no-ble ar-my, men and boys, The ma-tron and the maid,

His blood-red ban-ner streams a-far: Who fol-lows in His train?
Who saw his Mas-ter in the sky, And called on Him to save:
A-round the Sav-iour's throne re-joice, In robes of light ar-rayed:

Who best can drink His cup of woe, Tri-um-phant o-ver pain;
Like Him, with par-don on his tongue, In midst of mor-tal pain,
They climbed the steep as-cent of heav'n Through per-il, toil, and pain;

Who, pa-tient, bears his cross be-low, He fol-lows in His train.
He prayed for them that did the wrong: Who fol-lows in his train?
O God, to us may grace be giv'n To fol-low in their train!

Stand Up, Stand Up for Jesus

George Duffield, Jr.

WEBB. 7.6.7.6.D.
George J. Webb

1. Stand up, stand up for Je - sus, Ye sol - diers of the cross;
2. Stand up, stand up for Je - sus, Stand in His strength a - lone;
3. Stand up, stand up for Je - sus, The strife will not be long;

Lift high His roy - al ban - ner, It must not suf - fer loss:
The arm of flesh will fail you, Ye dare not trust your own:
This day the noise of bat - tle, The next the vic - tor's song:

From vic - t'ry un - to vic - t'ry His ar - my shall He lead,
Put on the gos - pel ar - mor, Each piece put on with pray'r;
To him that o - ver - com - eth A crown of life shall be;

Till ev - 'ry foe is van - quished, And Christ is Lord in - deed.
Where du - ty calls or dan - ger, Be nev - er want - ing there.
He, with the King of glo - ry, Shall reign e - ter - nal - ly.

180   For All the Saints

SINE NOMINE. 10.10.10. *with Alleluias*

William W. How   *Ralph Vaughan Williams*

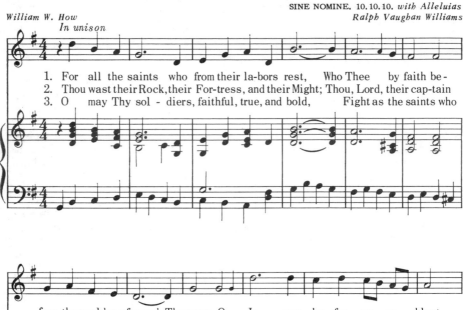

1. For all the saints who from their la-bors rest, Who Thee by faith be-
2. Thou wast their Rock, their For-tress, and their Might; Thou, Lord, their cap-tain
3. O may Thy sol - diers, faithful, true, and bold, Fight as the saints who

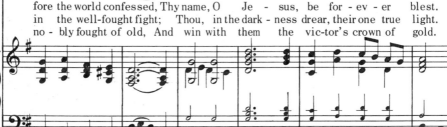

fore the world confessed, Thy name, O Je - sus, be for - ev - er blest.
in the well-fought fight; Thou, in the dark - ness drear, their one true light.
no - bly fought of old, And win with them the vic-tor's crown of gold.

Al - le-lu - ia! Al - le-lu - ia!
Al - le-lu - ia! Al - le-lu - ia!
Al - le-lu - ia! Al - le-lu - ia!

Mine Eyes Have Seen the Glory

BATTLE HYMN. *Irregular with Refrain*

Julia Ward Howe

American Folk Song

1. Mine eyes have seen the glo-ry of the com-ing of the Lord; He is
2. I have seen Him in the watchfires of a hun-dred cir-cling camps; They have
3. In the beau-ty of the lil-ies, Christ was born a-cross the sea, With a

tram-pling out the vintage where the grapes of wrath are stored; He hath loosed the
build-ed Him an al-tar in the eve-ning dews and damps; I can read His
glo-ry in His bos-om that trans-fig-ures you and me; As He died to

fate-ful light-ning of His ter-ri-ble swift sword; His truth is march-ing on.
righteous sen-tence by the dim and flar-ing lamps; His day is march-ing on.
make men ho-ly, let us die to make men free, While God is march-ing on.

REFRAIN

Glo-ry! glo-ry, hal-le-lu-jah! Glo-ry! glo-ry, hal-le-lu-jah!

Glo-ry! glo-ry, hal-le-lu-jah! Our God is march-ing on.

182

The Master Hath Come

Sarah Doudney

ASH GROVE. 12.11.12.11.D.
Welsh Melody

1. The Mas-ter hath come, and He calls us to fol-low The track of the
2. The Mas-ter hath called us; the road may be drear-y, And dan-gers and
3. The Mas-ter hath called us, in life's ear-ly morn-ing, With spir-its as

foot-prints He leaves on our way; Far o-ver the moun-tain and
sor-rows are strewn on the track; But God's Ho-ly Spir-it shall
fresh as the dew on the sod: We turn from the world, with its

through the deep hol-low, The path leads us on to the man-sions of day:
com - fort the wea-ry; We fol-low the Sav-iour and can-not turn back;
smiles and its scorn-ing, To cast in our lot with the peo-ple of God:

The Mas - ter hath called us, the children who fear Him, Who march 'neath Christ's
The Mas - ter hath called us: though doubt and temp-ta - tion May com-pass our
The Mas - ter hath called us, His sons and His daugh-ters, We plead for His

ban - ner, His own lit - tle band; We love Him and seek Him, we
jour - ney, we cheer-ful - ly sing: "Press on - ward, look up - ward," thro'
bless-ing and trust in His love; And through the green pas-tures, be-

long to be near Him, And rest in the light of His beau-ti-ful land.
much trib-u - la-tion; The chil-dren of Zi - on must fol-low their King.
side the still wa-ters, He'll lead us at last to His king-dom a - bove.

183   Serve the Lord with Gladness

B. B. McKinney

LEE. 6, 5, 6, 5, 6, 5, 6, 4, *with Refrain*
B. B. McKinney

1. "Serve the Lord with gladness" In our works and ways, Come be-fore His
2. "Serve the Lord with gladness," Thankful all the while For His ten - der
3. "Serve the Lord with gladness," This shall be our theme, As we walk to-

pres-ence With our songs of praise; Un - to Him our Mak - er
mer -cies, For His lov - ing smile: Bless - ed truth en - dur - ing,
geth - er In His love su - preme: Lis - tening, ev - er lis - tening

We would pledge a - new Life's supreme de - vo - tion To serv - ice true.
Al - ways just the same, We will serve with glad-ness And praise His name.
For the still, small voice, His sweet will so pre-cious Will be our choice.

REFRAIN

"Serve Him with glad-ness," En-ter His courts with song; To our Cre-

© Copyright 1959. Renewal. Broadman Press. All rights reserved. International copyright secured.

a - tor True prais-es be-long: Great is His mer - cy,

Won-der-ful is His name, We glad-ly serve Him, His great love pro-claim.

O Master, Let Me Walk with Thee 184

Washington Gladden

MARYTON. L.M.
H. Percy Smith

1. O Mas-ter, let me walk with Thee In low-ly paths of serv - ice free;
2. Help me the slow of heart to move By some clear, win-ning word of love;
3. Teach me Thy pa-tience; still with Thee In clos-er, dear-er com - pa - ny,
4. In hope that sends a shin-ing ray Far down the fu-ture's broad'ning way,

Tell me Thy se-cret, help me bear The strain of toil, the fret of care.
Teach me the way-ward feet to stay, And guide them in the homeward way.
In work that keeps faith sweet and strong, In trust that triumphs o - ver wrong.
In peace that on - ly Thou canst give, With Thee, O Mas-ter, let me live.

185   O Master Workman of the Race

Jay T. Stocking

AMESBURY. C.M.D.
Uzziah C. Burnap

1. O Mas - ter Work - man of the race, Thou Man of Gal - i - lee,
2. O Car - pen - ter of Naz - a - reth, Build - er of life di - vine,
3. O Thou who dost the vi - sion send, And giv - est each his task,

Who, with the eyes of ear - ly youth, E - ter - nal things didst see;
Who shap - est man to God's own law, Thy - self the fair de - sign,
And with the task suf - fi - cient strength: Show us Thy will, we ask;

We thank Thee for Thy boy - hood faith That shone Thy whole life through:
Build us a tow'r of Christ - like height, That we the land may view,
Give us a con - science bold and good; Give us a pur - pose true,

"Did ye not know it is My work My Fa - ther's work to do?"
And see, like Thee, our no - blest work, Our Fa - ther's work to do.
That it may be our high - est joy Our Fa - ther's work to do. A - MEN.

Words from *New Worship and Song.* The Pilgrim Press, publisher.

A Song of Youth

HOBBS. 6. 5. 6. 5. 6. 5. 7. 5.

Novella D. Preston

William J. Reynolds

1. For - ward in the serv - ice Of our Lord and King,
2. Learn - ing of the Mas - ter, And His will to do,
3. Loy - al to our Mas - ter, Here we take our stand,

We will work and wor - ship And His prais - es sing.
Joy - ful - ly we pledge Him Hand and heart so true.
Read - y to o - bey Him, Heed - ing His com - mand:

As we trust the Sav - iour, Cap - tain of our youth,
Mind and soul and bod - y Un - to Him we give;
"Think of thy Cre - a - tor In thy days of youth,

He will lead to vic - to - ry In the fight for truth.
Faith - ful in His serv - ice Dai - ly we will live.
While the years are fruit - ful In the quest for truth."

© Copyright 1964, Broadman Press. All rights reserved. International copyright secured.

Our Best

TULLAR. 6.4.6.4.D. *with Refrain*
Grant Colfax Tullar

S.C. Kirk

1. Hear ye the Master's call, "Give Me thy best!" For, be it great or small,
2. Wait not for men to laud, Heed not their slight; Winning the smile of God

That is His test. Do then the best you can, Not for re-ward, Not for the
Brings its de-light! Aid-ing the good and true Ne'er goes un-blest, All that we

REFRAIN

praise of man, But for the Lord.
think or do, Be it the best. Ev-'ry work for Je-sus will be blest,

But He asks from ev-'ry-one His best. Our tal-ents may be few,

These may be small, But un-to Him is due Our best, our all.

Copyright 1912 by Tullar-Meredith Co. Renewed 1939 by Lorenz Publishing Co. International copyright secured. Used by permission.

O Men of God, Go Forth to Win

188

VILLARS. L.M.
Eric Thiman

Thomas Tiplady

1. O men of God, go forth to win The world for Je-sus Christ your Lord; With faith that glows, and love that burns, Pro-claim to all His gra-cious Word.

2. To North and South, to East and West, Go forth in Christ's most ho-ly Name; On ev-'ry hill a bea-con light, And set the world with truth a-flame.

3. Let noth-ing daunt your ar-dor pure, Nor turn you from your pur-pose great; To save a world Christ sends you out, And for your mes-sage mil-lions wait.

4. On Cal-va-ry the Sav-iour died For ev-'ry man of ev-'ry race; 'Tis yours to make the good news known, And be the chan-nels of His grace.

Words copyright by Thomas Tiplady, Used by permission of the Hymn Society of America.
Music © Copyright 1964, Broadman Press. All rights reserved. International copyright secured.

189 Heralds of Christ

Laura S. Copenhaver

NATIONAL HYMN. 10.10.10.10.
George W. Warren

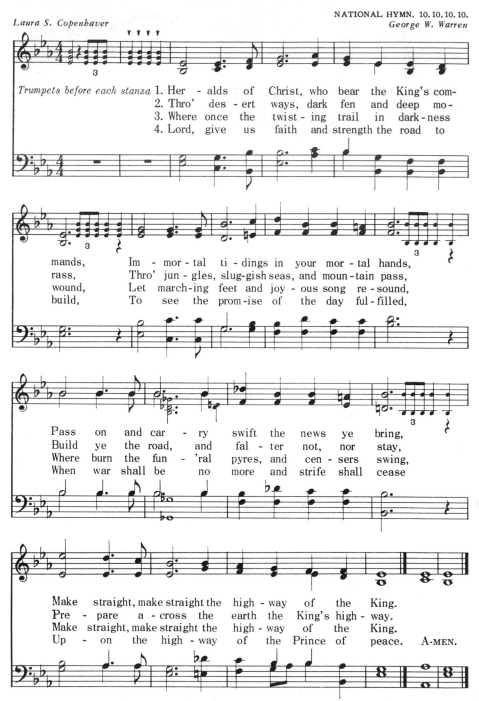

Trumpets before each stanza

1. Her - alds of Christ, who bear the King's com-
2. Thro' des - ert ways, dark fen and deep mo-
3. Where once the twist - ing trail in dark - ness
4. Lord, give us faith and strength the road to

mands, Im - mor - tal ti - dings in your mor - tal hands,
rass, Thro' jun - gles, slug-gish seas, and moun - tain pass,
wound, Let march-ing feet and joy - ous song re - sound,
build, To see the prom - ise of the day ful - filled,

Pass on and car - ry swift the news ye bring,
Build ye the road, and fal - ter not, nor stay,
Where burn the fun - 'ral pyres, and cen - sers swing,
When war shall be no more and strife shall cease

Make straight, make straight the high - way of the King.
Pre - pare a - cross the earth the King's high - way.
Make straight, make straight the high - way of the King.
Up - on the high - way of the Prince of peace. A-MEN.

O Zion, Haste

Mary A. Thomson

TIDINGS. 11.10.11.10. *with Refrain*
James Walch

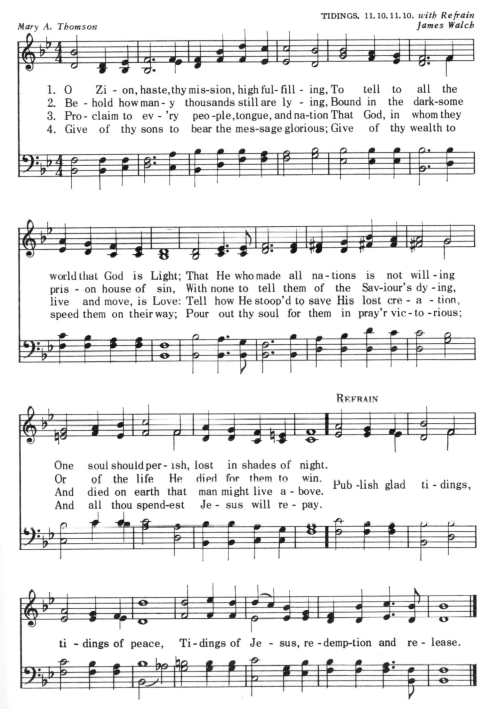

1. O Zi - on, haste, thy mis-sion, high ful- fill - ing, To tell to all the
2. Be - hold how man- y thousands still are ly - ing, Bound in the dark-some
3. Pro - claim to ev - 'ry peo - ple, tongue, and na-tion That God, in whom they
4. Give of thy sons to bear the mes-sage glorious; Give of thy wealth to

world that God is Light; That He who made all na - tions is not will - ing
pris - on house of sin, With none to tell them of the Sav-iour's dy - ing,
live and move, is Love: Tell how He stoop'd to save His lost cre - a - tion,
speed them on their way; Pour out thy soul for them in pray'r vic - to - rious;

REFRAIN

One soul should per - ish, lost in shades of night.
Or of the life He died for them to win.
And died on earth that man might live a - bove. Pub - lish glad ti - dings,
And all thou spend-est Je - sus will re - pay.

ti - dings of peace, Ti - dings of Je - sus, re - demp-tion and re - lease.

191 We've a Story to Tell

MESSAGE. 10.8.8.7.7. *with Refrain*

H. Ernest Nichol

H. Ernest Nichol, ad.

1. We've a sto-ry to tell to the na-tions, That shall
2. We've a song to be sung to the na-tions, That shall
3. We've a mes-sage to give to the na-tions, That the
4. We've a Sav-iour to show to the na-tions, Who the

turn their hearts to the right, A sto-ry of truth and mer-cy,
lift their hearts to the Lord, A song that shall con-quer e-vil,
Lord who reign-eth a-bove Hath sent us His Son to save us,
path of sor-row hath trod, That all of the world's great peo-ples

A sto-ry of peace and light, A sto-ry of peace and light.
And shat-ter the spear and sword, And shat-ter the spear and sword.
And show us that God is love, And show us that God is love.
May come to the truth of God, May come to the truth of God!

REFRAIN

For the dark-ness shall turn to dawn-ing, And the dawn-ing to noon-day bright,

And Christ's great kingdom shall come on earth, The king-dom of love and light.

Christ for the World We Sing 192

CUTTING. 6.6.4.6.6.6.4.

Samuel Wolcott

William F. Sherwin

1. Christ for the world we sing; The world to Christ we bring,
   With lov - ing zeal; The poor and them that mourn, The faint and
   o - ver - borne, Sin - sick and sor - row - worn, Whom Christ doth heal.

2. Christ for the world we sing; The world to Christ we bring,
   With fer - vent prayer; The way - ward and the lost, By rest-less
   pas - sion tossed, Re - deemed, at count-less cost, From dark de - spair.

3. Christ for the world we sing; The world to Christ we bring,
   With one ac - cord; With us the work to share, With us re -
   proach to dare, With us the cross to bear, For Christ our Lord.

4. Christ for the world we sing; The world to Christ we bring,
   With joy - ful song; The new - born souls, whose days, Re - claimed from
   er - ror's ways, In - spired with hope and praise, To Christ be - long.

193 Send Me, O Lord, Send Me

SURABAJA. 8.6.8.6.8.8.8.6.
Indonesian Folk Tune
Arr. by James Bigelow

Ross Coggins

1. O God of might, O Son of light, O Ho-ly Spir-it sweet,
2. With ho-ly fire my heart in-spire Thy Spir-it's sword to wield;
3. O that in me my Lord may see A bear-er of the name;

Thy church ex-pand till all shall stand At Je-sus' pierc-ed feet.
With bor-rowed might I'll take Thy light, Till dark-ness' doom be sealed.
That men may see His love so free, From age to age the same.

Let all who once Thy Son dis-owned Re-joice to see Him now en-throned;
If oth-ers stop to count the cost, For fear of earth-ly treas-ures lost,
Be this my ev-er-last-ing song, He took up-on Him-self my wrong,

Yet while one stray-ing soul there be, Send me, O Lord, send me.
I'll count it gain to die for Thee; Send me, O Lord, send me.
And cried while fac-ing Cal-va-ry, "Send Me, O Lord, send Me."

© Copyright 1956, Broadman Press. All rights reserved. International copyright secured.

Where Cross the Crowded Ways of Life   194

Frank Mason North

GERMANY. L.M.
From William Gardiner's "Sacred Melodies," 1815

1. Where cross the crowd - ed ways of life,
2. In haunts of wretch - ed - ness and need,
3. From ten - der child - hood's help - less - ness,
4. O Mas - ter, from the moun - tain side,
5. Till sons of men shall learn Thy love

Where sound the cries of race and clan,
On shad - ow'd thresh - olds dark with fears,
From wo - man's grief, man's bur - den'd toil,
Make haste to heal the hearts of pain;
And fol - low where Thy feet have trod;

A - bove the noise of self - ish strife,
From paths where hide the lures of greed,
From fam - ish'd souls, from sor - row's stress,
A - mong these rest - less throngs a - bide;
Till glo - rious from Thy heav'n a - bove

We hear Thy voice, O Son of man!
We catch the vi - sion of Thy tears.
Thy heart has nev - er known re - coil.
O tread the cit - y's streets a - gain,
Shall come the cit - y of our God.   A - MEN.

195

I Love to Tell the Story

Katherine Hankey

HANKEY. 7.6.7.6.D. *with Refrain*
William G. Fischer

1. I love to tell the sto - ry Of un - seen things a - bove, Of
2. I love to tell the sto - ry; 'Tis pleas-ant to re - peat What
3. I love to tell the sto - ry; For those who know it best Seem

Je - sus and His glo - ry, Of Je - sus and His love: I love to
seems each time I tell it, More won - der - ful - ly sweet: I love to
hun - ger - ing and thirst-ing To hear it, like the rest: And when in

tell the sto - ry Be - cause I know 'tis true; It sat - is - fies my
tell the sto - ry, For some have nev - er heard The mes - sage of sal -
scenes of glo - ry I sing the new, new song, 'Twill be the old, old

REFRAIN

long-ings As noth - ing else can do.
va - tion From God's own ho - ly Word. I love to tell the sto - ry, 'Twill
sto - ry That I have loved so long.

be my theme in glo-ry To tell the old, old sto-ry of Je-sus and His love.

Let the Saviour's Gentle Call

196

CULBACH. 7.7.7.7.
"Heilige Seelenlust," 1657

Anonymous

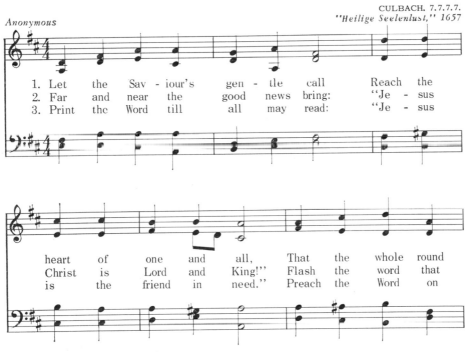

1. Let the Sav - iour's gen - tle call Reach the
2. Far and near the good news bring: "Je - sus
3. Print the Word till all may read: "Je - sus

heart of one and all, That the whole round
Christ is Lord and King!" Flash the word that
is the friend in need." Preach the Word on

world may know Christ is King, and Christ a - lone.
God is near O'er the air till all may hear.
ev - 'ry shore Till all men do God a - dore.

Children Who Live Across the Sea

William Grime

IRVING. L.M.
William Grime

1. Chil - dren who live a - cross the sea,
2. Chil - dren who pray a - cross the sea,
3. Chil - dren who work a - cross the sea,

What - e'er your race or col - or be,
What - e'er your race or col - or be,
What - e'er your race or col - or be,

Let us to - geth - er sing our praise
Let us to - geth - er kneel and say,
Let us to - geth - er try to make

To God our Fa - ther all our days.
"Our Fa - ther, bless each one to - day."
A bet - ter world, for Je - sus' sake. A - MEN.

Copyright © 1949, 1955 by Carl Fischer, Inc., New York. International copyright secured. All rights reserved including public performance for profit.

Tell the Blessed Tidings

COWDEN. 11.11.11.11.
Talmage W. Dean

Emily H. Miller, alt.

1. Tell the bless-ed ti - dings, chil -dren of the King,
2. Tell the bless-ed ti - dings, ye whose ears have heard;
3. Bear the bless-ed ti - dings, o - ver land and sea;

With your glad ho - san - nas make the morn-ing ring;
Tell the hun - gry na - tions wait-ing for the Word:
Lo, the morn - ing break-eth, and the shad-ows flee!

Songs of His sal - va - tion nev - er -more shall cease;
Christ the world's Re - deem - er, Sav - iour, Guide, and Friend!
Who - so - ev - er hear - eth speed the news a - long,

Crown Him with your prais - es, hail Him Prince of peace.
His the pow'r and glo - ry, king - dom with - out end!
Join with men and an - gels, in sal - va - tion's song.

Music © Copyright 1964, Broadman Press. All rights reserved. International copyright secured.

199 Jesus Shall Reign Where'er the Sun

Isaac Watts

DUKE STREET. L.M.
John Hatton

1. Je - sus shall reign wher - e'er the sun Does his suc-
ces - sive jour - neys run; His king-dom spread from shore to shore,
Till moons shall wax and wane no more.

2. From north to south the prin - ces meet To pay their
hom - age at His feet; While west-ern em - pires own their Lord,
And sav - age tribes at - tend His word.

3. To Him shall end - less pray'r be made, And end - less
prais - es crown His head; His name like sweet per - fume shall rise
With ev - 'ry morn - ing sac - ri - fice.

4. Peo - ple and realms of ev - 'ry tongue Dwell on His
love with sweet - est song, And in - fant voic - es shall pro - claim
Their ear - ly bless - ings on His name. A-MEN.

200 In Christ There Is No East or West

John Oxenham

ST. PETER. C.M.
Alexander R. Reinagle

1. In Christ there is no East or West, In Him no South or North;
2. In Him shall true hearts ev - 'ry-where Their high com - mun - ion find;
3. Join hands, then, brothers of the faith, What-e'er your race may be:
4. In Christ now meet both East and West, In Him meet South and North:

(continuation of previous hymn)

But one great fel-low-ship of love Through-out the whole wide earth.
His serv-ice is the gold-en cord, Close bind-ing all man-kind.
Who serves my Fa-ther as a son Is sure-ly kin to me.
All Christ-ly souls are one in Him, Through-out the whole wide earth.

Let the Song Go Round the Earth 201

MOEL LLYS. 7.5.7.5.7.7.

Sarah G. Stock

Sarah G. Stock

1. Let the song go round the earth, Je-sus Christ is Lord!
2. Let the song go round the earth, From the eas-tern sea,
3. Let the song go round the earth, Where the sum-mer smiles;
4. Let the song go round the earth, Je-sus Christ is King!

Sound his prais-es, tell His worth, Be His name a-dored;
Where the day-light has its birth, Glad and bright and free;
Let the notes of ho-ly mirth Break from dis-tant isles;
With the sto-ry of His worth Let the whole earth ring;

Ev-'ry clime and ev-'ry tongue Join the grand, the glo-rious song!
Chi-na's mil-lions join the strains, Waft them on to In-dia's plains.
In-land for-ests, dark and dim, Ice-bound coasts give back the hymn.
Him cre-a-tion all a-dore Ev-er-more and ev-er-more.

202   A Song of Praise

ST. JOHN. C.M.D.
Brazilian Folk Tune
Arranged by David P. Appleby

Bill F. Leach

1. Let praise to God go round the earth, A song of glad-ness ring; Let
2. Let praise to God go round the earth! Wher-ev-er man is found To the

Zi - on's chil-dren praise Their Mak-er and their King. Yea,
east, to the west, north and south, Let praise to God a - bound. Sound

let them praise the bless-ed One In ev -'ry land and tongue; By
forth His love, His mer -cies tell, Sal - va - tion loud pro - claim, Till

boys and girls of ev -'ry race, Let Je - sus' name be sung.
men of ev -'ry birth Shall bless His ho - ly name.

© Copyright 1962, 1964, Broadman Press. All rights reserved. International copyright secured.

How Wondrous and Great

BEGONE, UNBELIEF. 10.10.11.11.
Early American Melody

203

Henry U. Onderdonk

1. How won-drous and great Thy works, God of praise!
2. To na-tions long dark Thy light shall be shown;

How just, King of saints, and true are Thy ways!
Their wor-ship and vows shall come to Thy throne;

Oh, who shall not fear Thee and hon-or Thy name?
Thy truths and Thy judg-ments shall spread all a-broad,

Thou on-ly art ho-ly, Thou on-ly su-preme.
Till earth's ev-'ry peo-ple con-fess Thee their God.

Arrangement used by permission Lee H. Bristol, Jr.

204 ## We Give Thee But Thine Own

ST. ANDREW. S.M.
Joseph Barnby

William W. How

1. We give Thee but Thine own, What-e'er the gift may be; All
2. May we Thy boun-ties thus As stew-ards true re-ceive, And
3. The cap-tive to re-lease, To God the lost to bring, To
4. And we be-lieve Thy word, Though dim our faith may be; What-

that we have is Thine a-lone, A trust, O Lord, from Thee.
glad-ly, as Thou bless-est us, To Thee our first fruits give.
teach the way of life and peace, It is a Christ-like thing.
e'er for Thine we do, O Lord, We do it un-to Thee. A-MEN.

The Wise May Bring Their Learning

205

Anonymous
From "The Book of Praise for Children," 1881

ELLON. 7.6.7.6.D.
George F. Root

1. The wise may bring their learn - ing, The rich may bring their wealth,
2. We'll bring Him hearts that love Him; We'll bring Him thank - ful praise,
3. We'll bring the lit - tle du - ties We have to do each day;

And some may bring their great - ness, And some bring strength and health;
And young souls meek - ly striv - ing To walk in ho - ly ways:
We'll try our best to please Him, At home, at school, at play:

We, too, would bring our treas - ures To of - fer to the King;
And these shall be the treas - ures We of - fer to the King,
And bet - ter are these treas - ures To of - fer to the King,

We have no wealth or learn - ing: What shall we chil - dren bring?
And these are gifts that e - ven The poor - est child may bring.
Than rich - est gifts with - out them; Yet these a child may bring.

206 Something for Thee

SOMETHING FOR JESUS. 6.4.6.4.6.6.6.4.

Sylvanus D. Phelps

Robert Lowry

1. Sav - iour, Thy dy - ing love Thou gav - est me,
Nor should I aught with-hold, Dear Lord, from Thee:
In love my soul would bow, My heart ful - fil its vow,
Some of - f'ring bring Thee now, Some - thing for Thee.

2. At the blest mer - cy seat, Plead - ing for me,
My fee - ble faith looks up, Je - sus, to Thee:
Help me the cross to bear, Thy won - drous love de-clare,
Some song to raise, or pray'r, Some - thing for Thee.

3. Give me a faith - ful heart, Like - ness to Thee,
That each de - part - ing day Hence - forth may see
Some work of love be - gun, Some deed of kind - ness done,
Some wan - d'rer sought and won, Some - thing for Thee.

4. All that I am and have, Thy gifts so free,
In joy, in grief, thro' life, Dear Lord, for Thee!
And when Thy face I see, My ran - som'd soul shall be,
Thro' all e - ter - ni - ty, Some - thing for Thee. A-MEN.

Thy Work, O God, Needs Many Hands 207

Calvin W. Laufer

MEDITATION. C.M.
John H. Gower

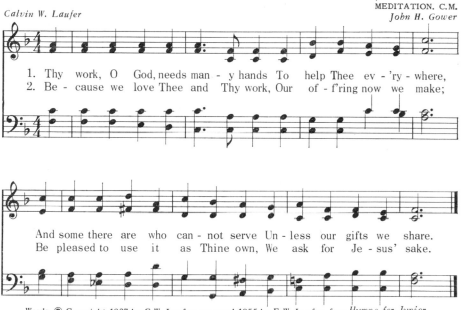

1. Thy work, O God, needs man - y hands To help Thee ev - 'ry - where,
2. Be - cause we love Thee and Thy work, Our of - f'ring now we make;

And some there are who can - not serve Un - less our gifts we share.
Be pleased to use it as Thine own, We ask for Je - sus' sake.

Words © Copyright 1927 by C.W. Laufer; renewed 1955 by E.W. Laufer; from *Hymns for Junior Worship*. Used by permission.

Our Gifts, Dear Lord, We Bring 208

Calvin W. Laufer

OUR GIFTS. C.M.
Carl F. Price

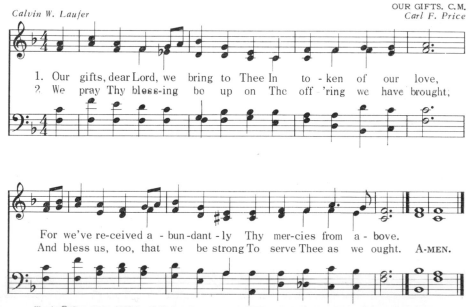

1. Our gifts, dear Lord, we bring to Thee In to - ken of our love,
2. We pray Thy bless - ing be up - on The off - 'ring we have brought;

For we've re - ceived a - bun - dant - ly Thy mer - cies from a - bove.
And bless us, too, that we be strong To serve Thee as we ought. A-MEN.

Words © Copyright 1927 by C.W. Laufer; renewed 1955 by E.B. Laufer. Music © Copyright 1927 by Presbyterian Board of Christian Education; renewed 1955; from *Junior Church School Hymnal*. Used by permission.

209   What Can I Give to Jesus

DEDICATION. 7.6.8.6.D.
From Alfred R. Gaul
Arr. by Loren R. Williams

Anonymous

1. What can I give to Je - sus, Who gave Him - self for me?
2. I'll give my voice to Je - sus, And seek through all my days
3. I'll give my wealth to Je - sus, Tho' lit - tle I pos - sess;

How can I show my love for Him, Who died on Cal - va - ry?
My ev - 'ry tal - ent con - se - crate To sing His joy - ous praise.
Take what I am and what I have, Dear Lord, ac - cept and bless.

I'll give my life to Je - sus, And calm - ly, glad - ly rest
I'll give my strength to Je - sus, Of head, of heart, and will;
What can I give to Je - sus, Who gave Him - self for me?

Each fu - ture hope and fond de - sire Up - on His lov - ing breast.
Go where He sends and ev - er strive His pur - pose to ful - fil.
I'll give my all to Je - sus, Who died on Cal - va - ry.

© Copyright 1956, Broadman Press. All rights reserved. International copyright secured.

Praise to God, Immortal Praise

210

DIX. 7.7.7.7.7.7.

Anna L. Barbauld

Arr. from Conrad Kocher

1. Praise to God, im-mor-tal praise, For the love that crowns our days;
2. All the plen-ty sum-mer pours; Au-tumn's rich o'er-flow-ing stores;
3. Peace, pros-per-i-ty and health, Pri-vate bliss, and pub-lic wealth,
4. As Thy pros-p'ring hand hath blest, May we give Thee of our best;

Boun-teous source of ev-'ry joy, Let Thy praise our tongues em-ploy;
Flocks that whit-en all the plain; Yel-low sheaves of rip-ened grain:
Knowl-edge with its gladd'ning streams, Pure re-li-gion's ho-lier beams:
And by deeds of kind-ly love For Thy mer-cies grate-ful prove;

All to Thee, our God, we owe, Source whence all our bless-ings flow.
Lord, for these our souls shall raise Grate-ful vows and sol-emn praise.
Lord, for these our souls shall raise Grate-ful vows and sol-emn praise.
Sing-ing thus thro' all our days, Praise to God, im-mor-tal praise.

211 Now Thank We All Our God

NUN DANKET. 6.7.6.7.6.6.6.6.

Martin Rinkart
Tr. by Catherine Winkworth

Johann Crüger
Harm. by Felix Mendelssohn

1. Now thank we all our God With heart and hands and voic - es,
2. O may this boun-teous God, Through all our life be near us,
3. All praise and thanks to God, The Fa - ther now be giv - en,

Who won - drous things hath done, In whom His world re - joic - es;
With ev - er joy - ful hearts And bless - ed peace to cheer us;
The Son, and Him who reigns With them in high - est heav - en,

Who, from our moth - er's arms, Hath blessed us on our way
And keep us in His grace, And guide us when per - plexed,
The one e - ter - nal God, Whom earth and heav'n a - dore;

With count-less gifts of love, And still is ours to - day.
And free us from all ills In this world and the next.
For thus it was, is now, And shall be ev - er - more. A-MEN.

We Come with Songs of Gladness

Anonymous

DONNELLY. 7.6.7.6.D.
Calvin W. Laufer

1. We come with songs of glad-ness To praise our God and King,
2. We praise Thee for earth's beau-ty, And for the sky's blue dome;
3. The an-gels lift their an-thems Of heav'n-ly joy on high,

And for His love and mer-cy Our grate-ful trib-ute bring.
We praise Thee for our coun-try; We praise Thee for our home;
And fill Thy courts with mu-sic In songs that nev-er die.

The bless-ings of His boun-ty Have crowned with joy our days;
We praise Thee for Thy gos-pel, And for a Sav-iour's love;
And when be-yond the riv-er We reach the cit-y fair,

Then sing we al-le-lu-ia, And thank-ful voic-es raise.
We praise Thee for the prom-ise Of end-less life a-bove.
We'll sing the song of glad-ness With sweet-er rap-ture there.

Music © Copyright 1927 by C. W. Laufer; renewed 1955 by E. B. Laufer; from *Junior Church School Hymnal*. Used by permission.

213 We Gather Together

Anonymous
Tr. by Theodore Baker

KREMSER. *Irregular*
Netherlands Folk Song
Arr. by Edward Kremser

1. We gath-er to-geth-er to ask the Lord's bless-ing,
2. Be-side us to guide us, our God with us join-ing,
3. We all do ex-tol Thee, Thou lead-er in bat-tle,

He chas-tens and has-tens His will to make known;
Or-dain-ing, main-tain-ing His king-dom di-vine;
And pray that Thou still our de-fend-er wilt be.

The wick-ed op-press-ing now cease from dis-tress-ing,
So from the be-gin-ning the fight we were win-ning,
Let Thy con-gre-ga-tion es-cape trib-u-la-tion;

Sing prais-es to His name, He for-gets not His own.
Thou, Lord, wast at our side: the glo-ry be Thine!
Thy name be ev-er praised: O Lord, make us free! A-MEN.

Come, Ye Thankful People, Come

ST. GEORGE'S, WINDSOR. 7.7.7.7.D.

Henry Alford

George J. Elvey

1. Come, ye thank-ful peo-ple, come, Raise the song of har-vest home!
2. We our-selves are God's own field, Fruit un-to His praise to yield;
3. For the Lord our God shall come, And shall take His har-vest home;

All is safe-ly gath-ered in, Ere the win-ter storms be-gin;
Wheat and tares to-geth-er sown Un-to joy or sor-row grown;
From His field shall purge a-way All that doth of-fend that day;

God, our Mak-er, doth pro-vide For our wants to be sup-plied:
First the blade, and then the ear, Then the full corn shall ap-pear;
Give His an-gels charge at last In the fire the tares to cast;

Come to God's own tem-ple, come, Raise the song of har-vest home.
Lord of har-vest! grant that we Whole-some grain and pure may be.
But the fruit-ful ears to store In His gar-ner ev-er-more.

215 Sing to the Lord of Harvest

John S. B. Monsell

NORTHAVEN. 7.6.7.6.
Jane M. Marshall

1. Sing to the Lord of har - vest, Sing songs of love and
2. By Him the roll - ing sea - sons In fruit - ful or - der
3. Bring to His sa - cred al - tar The gifts His good - ness
4. Your hearts lay down be - fore Him When at His feet ye

praise; With joy - ful hearts and voic - es Your
move; Oh, sing to the Lord of har - vest, A
gave, The gold - en sheaves of har - vest, The
fall; And with your lives a - dore Him Who

al - - le - lu - ias raise.
song of hap - py love.
souls He died to save.
gave His life for all.

© Copyright 1960, 1964, Broadman Press. All rights reserved. International copyright secured.

My Country, 'Tis of Thee

216

AMERICA. 6.6.4.6.6.6.4.
Anonymous

Samuel F. Smith

1. My coun - try, 'tis of thee, Sweet land of lib - er - ty,
2. My na - tive coun - try, thee, Land of the no - ble free,
3. Let mu - sic swell the breeze, And ring from all the trees
4. Our fa - thers' God, to Thee, Au - thor of lib - er - ty,

Of thee I sing: Land where my fa - thers died, Land of the
Thy name I love: I love thy rocks and rills, Thy woods and
Sweet free - dom's song: Let mor - tal tongues a - wake; Let all that
To Thee we sing: Long may our land be bright With free - dom's

pil - grims' pride, From ev - 'ry moun - tain - side Let free - dom ring!
tem - pled hills; My heart with rap - ture thrills Like that a - bove.
breathe par - take; Let rocks their si - lence break, The sound pro - long.
ho - ly light; Pro - tect us by Thy might, Great God, our King!

The Star-Spangled Banner

Francis Scott Key

NATIONAL ANTHEM. *Irregular with Refrain*
Anonymous

1. Oh, say, can you see, by the dawn's ear - ly light, What so
2. Oh, thus be it ev - er when free men shall stand Be -

proud - ly we hailed at the twi - light's last gleam - ing, Whose broad
tween their loved homes and the war's des - o - la - tion; Blest with

stripes and bright stars, thro' the per - il - ous fight, O'er the ramparts we watched,
vic - t'ry and peace, may the heav'n-rescued land Praise the Pow'r that hath made

were so gal - lant - ly stream-ing? And the rock - ets' red glare, the bombs
and pre-served us a na - tion! Then con - quer we must, when our

burst-ing in air Gave proof thro' the night that our flag was still there.
cause it is just; And this be our mot-to: "In God is our trust!"

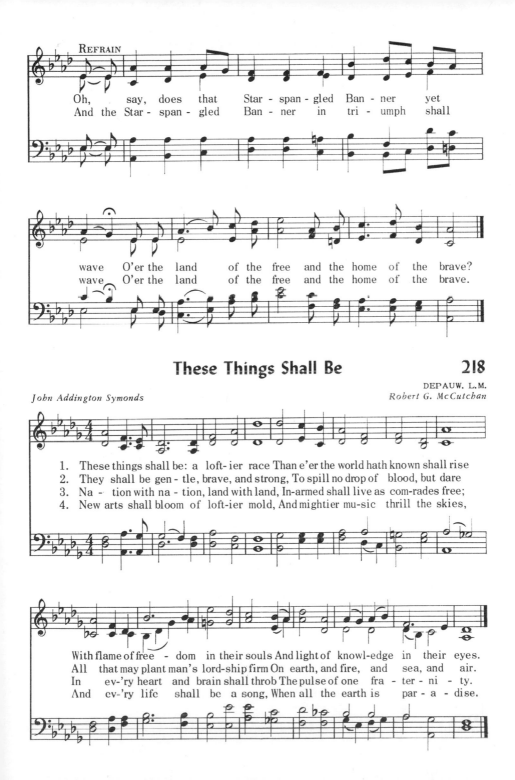

REFRAIN

Oh, say, does that Star - span - gled Ban - ner yet
And the Star - span - gled Ban - ner in tri - umph shall

wave O'er the land of the free and the home of the brave?
wave O'er the land of the free and the home of the brave.

These Things Shall Be

218

DEPAUW. L.M.
Robert G. McCutchan

John Addington Symonds

1. These things shall be: a loft-ier race Than e'er the world hath known shall rise
2. They shall be gen - tle, brave, and strong, To spill no drop of blood, but dare
3. Na - tion with na - tion, land with land, In-armed shall live as com-rades free;
4. New arts shall bloom of loft-ier mold, And mightier mu-sic thrill the skies,

With flame of free - dom in their souls And light of knowl-edge in their eyes.
All that may plant man's lord-ship firm On earth, and fire, and sea, and air.
In ev'ry heart and brain shall throb The pulse of one fra - ter - ni - ty.
And ev'ry life shall be a song, When all the earth is par - a - dise.

America the Beautiful

MATERNA. C.M.D.

Katharine Lee Bates

Samuel A. Ward

1. O beau-ti-ful for spa-cious skies, For am-ber waves of grain,
2. O beau-ti-ful for pil-grim feet, Whose stern, im-pas-sioned stress
3. O beau-ti-ful for he-roes proved In lib-er-at-ing strife,
4. O beau-ti-ful for pa-triot dream That sees, be-yond the years,

For pur-ple moun-tain maj-es-ties A-bove the fruit-ed plain!
A thor-ough-fare for free-dom beat A-cross the wil-der-ness!
Who more than self their coun-try loved, And mer-cy more than life!
Thine al-a-bas-ter cit-ies gleam, Un-dimmed by hu-man tears!

A-mer-i-ca! A-mer-i-ca! God shed His grace on thee,
A-mer-i-ca! A-mer-i-ca! God mend thine ev-'ry flaw,
A-mer-i-ca! A-mer-i-ca! May God thy gold re-fine,
A-mer-i-ca! A-mer-i-ca! God shed His grace on thee,

And crown thy good with broth-er-hood From sea to shin-ing sea.
Con-firm thy soul in self-con-trol, Thy lib-er-ty in law.
Till all suc-cess be no-ble-ness, And ev-'ry gain di-vine.
And crown thy good with broth-er-hood From sea to shin-ing sea.

Doxology

220

Thomas Ken

OLD 100th. L.M.
From the "Genevan Psalter," 1551

Praise God, from whom all blessings flow; Praise Him, all crea-tures here be - low;

Praise Him a - bove, ye heav'nly host; Praise Father, Son, and Ho - ly Ghost. A-MEN.

221 Glory Be to the Father

GLORIA PATRI
From Henry W. Greatorex' "Collection," 1851

Glo - ry be to the Fa - ther, and to the Son, and to the

Ho - ly Ghost; As it was in the be - gin - ning, is now, and ev - er

shall be, world with - out end. A - men, A - men.

222 O Worship the Lord

PORTER. *Irregular*
Robert G. McCutchan

Psalm 96:9

O wor - ship the Lord in the beau - ty of ho - li - ness;

Music copyright 1963. Renewal. The Methodist Book Concern. Used by permission.

Serve Him with glad - ness, all the earth. A - MEN.

All Things Are Thine 223

GERMANY. L.M.

John G. Whittier *William Gardiner's "Sacred Melodies," 1815*

All things are Thine; no gift have we, Lord of all gifts, to

of - fer Thee, And hence, with grate - ful hearts to - day,

Thy own be - fore Thy feet we lay. A - MEN.

224   Grant Us, Lord, the Grace of Giving

STUTTGART. 8.7.8.7.
Christian F. Witt

Grant us, Lord, the grace of giv-ing, With a spir-it large and free,

That our-selves and all our liv-ing We may of-fer un-to Thee. A-MEN.

225   Bless Thou the Gifts

CANONBURY. L.M.
Robert Schumann

Samuel Longfellow

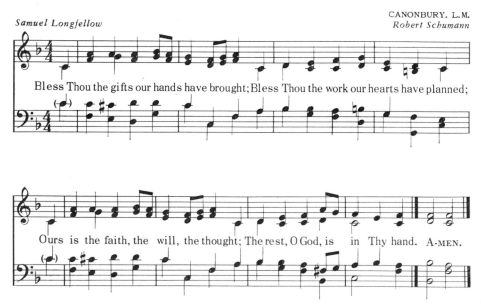

Bless Thou the gifts our hands have brought; Bless Thou the work our hearts have planned;

Ours is the faith, the will, the thought; The rest, O God, is in Thy hand. A-MEN.

Lead Me, Lord

226

Psalm 5:8

Samuel S. Wesley

Lead me, Lord, lead me in Thy right - eous - ness.

Make Thy way plain be - fore my face. A - MEN.

Let the Words of My Mouth

227

Psalm 19:14

S. D. Lonyer

Let the words of my mouth, and the med - i - ta - tion of my heart, be ac -

cept - a - ble in Thy sight, O Lord, my strength, and my Re - deem - er. A - MEN.

228

Teach Us How to Pray

ST. FLAVIAN. C.M.
From John Day's "Psalter," 1562

Anonymous

Lord, Je - sus, teach us how to pray, And then ac - cept our prayers;

For Thou cans't hear the words we say, For Thou art ev - 'ry - where. A-MEN.

229

Almighty Father, Hear Our Prayer

Felix Mendelssohn

Al - might - y Fa - ther, hear our prayer; and

bless all souls that wait be - fore Thee. A-MEN.

Hear Our Prayer, O Lord

George Whelpton

Hear our prayer, O Lord, Hear our prayer, O Lord;

In - cline Thine ear to us, And grant us Thy peace. A-MEN.

May the Grace of Christ Our Saviour

STUTTGART. 8.7.8.7.
Christian F. Witt

John Newton

May the grace of Christ our Sav - iour And the Fa - ther's bound-less love,

With the Ho - ly Spir - it's fa - vor, Rest up - on us from a - bove. A-MEN.

INDEXES

Index of Authors, Translators, Composers, Arrangers, and Sources of Hymns

Alphabetical Index of Tunes

Topical Index

(Titles are in caps and small caps; first lines in lower case type)

Index of First Lines and Titles

(Titles are in caps and small caps; first lines in lower case type)

223

224